HUN

Once back home in the Outback, Stephanie was beginning to realise that her engagement to Marcus was a mistake. And that had nothing to do with the infuriating Boyd Ballinger— who could raise her temperature to boiling point just by looking at her . . .

Books you will enjoy
by MARGARET WAY

HOUSE OF MEMORIES

Years ago, Dana Merriman had been the typical Australian aristocratic rich girl, and Nick McMasters the poor boy who had dared to love her, but nothing had come of it. Now their positions were reversed; Dana had lost her home and her money, and Nick had come back, a self-made millionaire. Had he anything on his mind but revenge?

ALMOST A STRANGER

A family feud had kept Skye and her grandfather apart for years, but now she had decided to heal the breach and had gone to visit him in Sydney. Only to find herself in the middle of another family feud—against herself—and fighting the disturbing attraction of Guy Reardon. . . .

A PLACE CALLED RAMBULARA

The predatory Lucinda Shieffield was nothing but trouble, Georgina thought worriedly, as she watched the other woman destroying her beloved brother's marriage. Why couldn't she content herself with her brother-in-law Quinn Shieffield, who could take a woman like Lucinda in his stride? But did Georgina really want to see Quinn get involved with Lucinda?

FALLEN IDOL

Everyone's idol, Dominic Grey was the son Grant Ingram had always longed for, and Claudia Ingram was the beautiful, accomplished daughter he was intensely proud of. Not surprisingly, his ambition was to see them marry, but one person stood between them— his wife!

HUNT
THE SUN

BY

MARGARET WAY

MILLS & BOON LIMITED
15–16 BROOK'S MEWS
LONDON W1A 1DR

First published in Great Britain 1984
by Mills & Boon Limited

© Margaret Way 1984

Australian copyright 1984
Philippine copyright 1985

ISBN 0 263 74910 X

Set in Monophoto Plantin 11 on 11 pt.
01–0185 – 49115

Made and printed in Great Britain by
Richard Clay (The Chaucer Press) Ltd,
Bungay, Suffolk

CHAPTER ONE

STEPHANIE stood on the verandah of the bungalow aware that panic, like so many shooting tendrils, was tightening its grip on her heart. It was sunset and the western sky was aflame, the dust hazed sun a pulsing blood red with an aureole of molten gold. At another time she would have found the sight splendid, now it seemed like the fiery prelude to nightmare. In another few minutes the sun would go down behind the Bandar escarpment and the short, spectacular twilight, the merest opalescent mauve flush, would lapse into deepest, blackest night.

Stephanie shuddered uncontrollably and wrapped her arms around her tense body. It had been a day of drawing, humid heat yet now when the sun was dying a peculiar chill invaded the wild country. She lifted her face to the massive bulk of the Bandar, etched in jagged purple against the rapidly pearling sky. It was estimated to be around 400 million years old, slashed by deep gorges and sacred to the nomadic aboriginals. Like Ayers Rock and the Olgas it was unique yet in the ghostly evening light it looked almost terrifying.

A flight of white cockatoos screeched overhead jangling her already overworked nerves. Myriads of birds were still coming into drink at the long line of billabongs of the old river. Clouds of rose-pink galahs and parrots, the noisy cockatoos with their sulphur yellow crests, hosts of budgerigars,

finches and all the little honey eaters. The
country after the improbable wet 'Dry' was in
startlingly good condition for which she was
doubly grateful and a few nights before they had
experienced a heavy rainstorm. Now countless
millions of wildflowers ran like wildfire over the
virulent green flats. They enveloped an enormous
area, turning the vast loneliness into a brilliant-
hued carpet, breast high in places, predominantly
pink—the pink of the narrow leafed parakeelya.
In the old days the camels of the Territory had
grazed it avidly and it was still excellent fodder
for the stock. Even a man could get moisture
from the succulent. Precious, lifesaving moisture.
In Australia, in particular, water was life but
there were large areas of Jandra distant from the
river and only three bores. Stephanie remembered
how Marcus only knew the location of one.

She was still holding herself tensely when her
uncle followed her out on to the verandah. He,
too, was under the weight of anxiety but he
placed a bracing arm around her shoulders.
'Don't you worry, Steph, he'll be here. He's an
intelligent, experienced man.'

'He knows *nothing* about the wild country,'
Stephanie murmured nervously.

'I tell you, my dear, he'll drive up in a few
moments.' Harry Sinclair spoke emphatically to
cover his own gnawing tensions. Drat the fella!
He hadn't really taken to his beloved Stephanie's
fiancé. And neither had Ellen. That was
important. Ellen had enormous intuitive powers.

'Oh, why oh why did we let him go?' Stephanie
actually breathed the words in her uncle's mind.

'Because he absolutely insisted, m'dear,' Harry
answered tersely. 'Your Aunt and I thought you

two had had a little falling-out. Don't tell me if you don't want to. We just thought there was a little tension. Obviously this isn't what he's used to—a lonely old cattle station. Maybe he just wanted to escape for a little while.'

'He's been gone for hours, Harry.'

Harry glared out at the bush violently. 'He'll be here.' He could find little comfort in his own positive attitude. 'I mean he's travelled all over the world. I can't possibly accept that he's lost himself when he said he wasn't going far. The stockboys are about. Old Jacky Crow. You don't think he'd be fool enough to take a swim in one of the lily lagoons?'

'Oh, God, Harry!' Stephanie shuddered.

'Tourist fella up here last year had a nasty encounter with a croc.' Harry scratched his chin, then looking at his niece winced for his own stupidity. 'I don't mean your fella, darlin'. He knows how to take good care of himself. Photographs wasn't it?'

'Yes. He's very interested in photography and the country is in prime condition. No one could believe those wildflowers unless they saw them.'

'And he didn't want you to go with him?' Harry marvelled. Any man that let Steph out of his sight for a moment had to be mad.

'We did have an argument,' Stephanie now confirmed.

The visit had not been a success. Marcus, head of the advertising agency where she worked, was essentially a man who liked his creature comforts, a luxurious apartment, gourmet food, a Mercedes coupé to get around in. These were the things he valued. Where Stephanie revelled in the exotica of Jandra, Marcus felt like a fish out of water and

one or two of his little witticisms had been quite
stinging. In fact, Stephanie had come to realise,
away from the office and the most urbane settings
Marcus had not shown up in a particularly
favourable light. Of course he had been perfectly
pleasant to Harry and Ellen but there was a
degree of condescension in the practised charm
and in private his comments had verged on
outright ridicule.

That above all had caused the argument.
Stephanie adored her aunt and uncle and was
fiercely protective of their little 'eccentricities'.
Besides she hadn't considered for one moment
Marcus would have so little sensibility as to
criticise them no matter what he privately
thought. After all, they were his hosts and she
was their niece. Criticising family could make or
break an engagement and Harry and Ellen were
all the family she had since her parents had been
killed in a light aircraft crash when she was barely
fourteen. Harry and Ellen were good people.
Better, they were the best.

'What is it, love?' Harry asked. 'We've always
been straight with one another. Can't you tell
me?'

'It's just that I don't know.' Stephanie quietly
slipped an arm around her uncle's waist. 'I
thought I was in love with Marcus.'

'But you think he's someone different out
here?'

'You're not seeing him at his best, Harry,'
Stephanie felt moved to protest. 'He's fantastically good at his job. He's only thirty-two years
old yet he's achieved a good deal. He's very
highly respected in the advertising world. He has
enormous merchandising flair and he knows how

to reward hard work and ambition. He's been very good to me.'

'And why not?' Harry glanced at her. From the moment she had arrived Stephanie had forsaken her glamorous city-image but even without her smart clothes and the glossy make-up she had an awful lot going for her—a beautiful figure and a flawless olive skin that had the glow of perfect health. She had masses of thick mahogany dark hair with a generous natural curl and where one expected dark eyes, Stephanie's were a deep and beautiful flower-blue—almost violet. So far as Harry was concerned Stephanie's looks belonged in a very special category and not only was she beautiful, she had brains. This fiancé she had brought up to them was the only mistake she had made. 'It would be very easy for a man to be nice to you,' Harry said.

'I'm good, Harry.'

'I know you are. If anyone can push through the barriers you can. Women are everything these days and why not? They've always been the managers.'

'Still not here yet?' Ellen pushed open the screen door looking worried.

'No, love.' Harry looked back over his shoulder.

'He was so certain he didn't want anybody to go with him,' Ellen clicked her tongue. 'Surely he wouldn't have wandered away from the jeep?'

'He hasn't got much longer to make it,' Stephanie looked up at the darkening sky. 'We should have been out looking before this.'

'He seemed the kind of man to disdain our help,' Ellen returned a little tartly. Ellen was a small, very spare woman with a tanned skin and silver-grey hair neatly twisted into a roll. She always wore pants and a shirt as her daily uniform and she radiated energy and a womanly determination. Now she was shaken by the same anxiety as Stephanie and Harry. Whatever Stephanie's fiancé's position in the city Ellen had the certain feeling he wouldn't know how to get anywhere in the bush. A man like that was born and bred to every comfort and convenience. Prepared to like and accept him, Ellen too had been disappointed in Stephanie's choice. He was good looking certainly and nimble-tongued, but at bottom Ellen considered he was dangerously superficial. Not what Ellen had expected at all.

By eight o'clock it was decided to send out a search party at first light. Jacky Crow came to the edge of the verandah and Harry explained what he wanted him to do. The Aboriginal tracker was no longer young but he was still better than any white man on the station. All the time Harry spoke the black man listened attentively then with a kind of self-effacing obeisance he disappeared into the night.

'I wonder if we shouldn't get onto Boyd?' Ellen asked.

'Oh, leave him out of it,' Stephanie said hastily. 'Boyd could do in minutes what might take us all day.'

Stephanie stood up and took several steps around the large, airy living room. She looked flustered but very lovely with colour running beneath her satiny cheeks. 'And I suppose it will only take him seconds to convey his contempt for our stupidity.'

'It's always the same here in the bush, love,' Harry said. 'It's difficult for the searching party not to get a little bit angry. There are rules and travellers are not supposed to break them. Your Marcus was only going to the lagoon but you heard what Jacky said, he saw the jeep heading out towards the Bandar. If Boyd or one of his men could take the chopper up chances are they could spot him early otherwise we'll have to take the horses out. There is the possibility too he'll come in at first light.'

'Oh, I hope so!' Stephanie said fervently.

As it was she was to lie awake with the howls of the dingos filtering through the eroded hills. The North was still the last wild frontier and she guessed a night alone in the near jungle would be a frightful experience for the ultra-civilised Marcus. Obviously he had become lost but as long as he stayed with the jeep the chopper should easily find him.

Marcus had not returned with the dawn and by eight o'clock Boyd Ballinger flew in.

Stephanie drew a deep breath and threw up her head as he walked towards the bungalow with Harry and Ellen flanking him on either side. His outline was unmistakable, something about the height, the breadth of shoulder and superbly disciplined leanness, the easy rhythm of his walk. He wasn't wearing a hat and his hair was jet black and lightly tousled by the wind, his face a dark bronze from the tropical sun and even at a distance she could catch the glint of his silver, contemptuous eyes. What else *was* it? Boyd Ballinger had always affected her violently. There seemed no way they could get on an easy, comfortable footing, yet Harry and Ellen took as much pride in him and his achievements as though he were their very own. In the north of the continent the Ballinger name was magic. It meant wealth and power and a great pioneering family. The Ballingers had been the first to stake out a claim on the beautiful, primitive North-West frontier. The Ballingers had been the first to build a mansion, a *true* mansion, in the middle of real jungle. A cause for wonder in those early days not only as to cost but the sheer incongruity of it. Where once nomadic blacks had built gunyahs of boughs and bark a stone mansion reminiscent of a French château now existed. The sort of thing to take hold of the mind and the imagination.

'How are you, Stephanie?' Boyd Ballinger greeted her without a smile and a long, penetrating scrutiny.

'It was good of you to come, Boyd.' Her response was as low-keyed as his was high-powered. It had always been that way. He a Ballinger, bred to a great heritage: she Harry Sinclair's orphaned little niece, the one-time romantic little fool. They were worlds apart and better so.

'Boyd would like to get away as soon as possible,' Harry explained. Whatever Boyd Ballinger wanted, he got. Harry was looking up at him as though he were the sun, moon and stars. He was bigger, taller than she remembered or Harry and Ellen were starting to shrink with age.

Just as she was studying him, he looked back at her acutely, the faintest mocking tug to his sculptured mouth. With so much given to him, wealth and privilege, vast land holdings, one might have thought the gods would stop short at physical endowments, but with a Ballinger nothing seemed to be the limit. He was stunningly handsome in the manner of a fallen angel; very dark and proud, a faintly intimidating cast to his aristocratic features. Until he smiled. Then the sensuous mouth moved and showed its beautiful shape. His teeth were very fine and white and the frosted silver-grey eyes lost their icy brilliance and imparted a devastating sparkle. He was a *marvellous* man and there wasn't another human being Stephanie feared more. Even looking at him was dangerous. She ought to know.

He defeated her by turning away deliberately. He began to question Harry about the last sighting of the missing man. Marcus might have been a stranger and not Stephanie's fiancé at all.

'Boyd will find him if anyone can,' Ellen murmured to Stephanie gently. 'You'll see the jeep from the air. He could even be making his way in. It's easy to become disoriented in the bush.'

'I'm coming with you, Boyd,' Stephanie intervened.

'If you like,' he retorted brusquely. He had never once asked why they had allowed Marcus to go off on his own but the unspoken question hung rather grimly in the air.

Ellen had retreated to the kitchen, now she came back with her best silver pot full of coffee. 'Time for a quick cup, Boyd?'

'If you pour it now, Ellen.' He threw Ellen a backward glance. 'Are you ready, Stephanie?'

'I am.' She didn't even bother to glance down at her clothes. Like Ellen she was dressed for action in a thin cotton shirt and riding pants, gear that suited her slender, taller than average figure. She had barely been able to eat breakfast herself,

now Ellen passed her another cup of coffee
silently. Ellen wasn't demonstrative as Harry was
but this didn't hinder the flow of love and
understanding between the two women. Ellen
knew how she felt.. On many scores. She even
knew the effect Boyd Ballinger had on her; the
vague antagonism and the over-awe, perhaps
inevitable with the comparison in their back-
grounds.

Five minutes later they were lifting over the
treetops heading west towards the Bandar.
Beyond that lay Ballinger country; a vast run
stretching to the sunset and beyond. It had been
a long time since she had been on Opal Downs,
five years, and she remembered Anne Ballinger's
cruelty as though it were yesterday. Of course she
wasn't a real Ballinger. She had married into the
family.

It had been easy for someone like Anne to
torture a young girl. In the ordinary manner
Stephanie would have been fortunate to gain
entrée to the magnificent homestead but Mrs
Elizabeth Ballinger, Boyd's mother, had taken
quite a fancy to Harry Sinclair's orphaned niece
and insisted that she be invited to all the young
gatherings on Opal. That last time had been a gala
ball to celebrate Cathy's twenty-first and the not
quite eighteen-year-old Stephanie had been
thrilled out of her mind to be invited. Harry and
Ellen had even bought her the most beautiful
dress! There wasn't anything on earth they
wouldn't do for her, yet the whole thing had
turned into a continuing torment. At twenty-
three Stephanie still convulsed away from it in
her mind though she was a vastly different girl
from the helpless little creature she had been

then. Anne Ballinger had turned a young girl's crush into something sordid and shameful and from that day on Stephanie had spun the first of many protective layers. She had never accepted an invitation to the homestead again though she and Harry and Ellen had continued to attend the great, annual Xmas barbecue and afterwards the polo match. One brush with fire had been enough and shortly afterwards Mrs Ballinger, a widow since Garth Ballinger had been killed in a freak accident on the station some years before, remarried and went to live in Melbourne with her new husband, an eminent Supreme Court judge.

Mix with your own kind. Like most maxims it was true.

Conversation was almost impossible in the helicopter but neither of them seemed inclined to even attempt it. Their main concentration was directed towards scanning the vast wilderness but all they saw was two stock men flushing out strays, cattle on the grazing places and a small band of kangaroos gathered at a lily-pond. The country on the edge of the Wet was densely green. With the rains the bush would burst into flower; the great mangoes, the poincianas with their great crimson arches, the golden cascara trees, the bougainvillea crimson, white and cerise, climbing like a brilliant parasite, the tulip trees that broke open their orange blooms. Along the curving billabongs she could see the magnificent profusion of lilies, the pink and the white and the sacred lotus blue. Pandanus curved spikily over the glowing rocks and in the shadow of the Bandar rubber trees and the silver cadjuput towered over wonderful palms and ferns and prolific flowering creepers. Down there it was luxuriant jungle and further away in the swamp lands, glassed over by dark emerald green water thickly sown with water lilies, was the haunt of the crocodiles. Once the whole swamp had been alive with them but so many had been shot out for their skins they were now protected and as Harry was beginning to say, ready for culling. For long hours now Stephanie had been constantly aware of a fairly recent tragedy Harry had referred to. Every now and again much to people's horror some human invaded the crocodiles watery habitat and paid for it with his life. Now as Stephanie lowered the fieldglasses she could see the whole area was crowded with birds—ibises, ducks, spoonbills, the great jabiru, large black-and-white storks and between the tall reeds a colony of brolgas.

Boyd brought the helicopter down closer over the thickly timbered area. A huge bull crocodile was sunning himself on a rocky outcrop, the very picture of contentment in his luxuriant wilderness setting.

Stephanie could not help it, she shuddered, even though her palms were damp with sweat. Marcus like everybody else had been fascinated by Harry's crocodile stories, some of them fairly tall, but Stephanie couldn't believe he would be rash enough to hunt after them for photographs. One needed an experienced bushman for that and always to be on the safe side, a gun. Yet tourists demonstrated every day they left caution behind when on holiday. *Nothing* could happen to them when on holiday whether in a strange city or the deceptively empty bush.

There was absolutely no sign of the jeep. Or so she thought until Boyd turned for another sweep of the massif foot. The escarpment was slashed by deep gorges and down between the cliffs in a rocky corridor perhaps twelve feet wide were the deeply grooved tracks of a vehicle on the almost white sand. Further on, she could just pick out the jeep, half-hidden by trees. Marcus had obviously decided to explore this fascinating place on foot. The cliffs stretched for miles, carved out by the roaring torrents of the Wet and superbly patterned with horizontal bands of colour. Marcus would have been drawn to their grand, sculptural beauty.

Boyd Ballinger made a sign to her that she understood. He was going to try for a landing and if Marcus were about and able to, he would surely come out. As it was, the chopper, banking in a high wide turn was disturbing the wildlife. Birds exploded from the lush riverine vegetation like wind-tossed flowers, a brilliant variety of colours through palest pastel to gaudy enamel and the agile wallabies were bounding away to cover.

There were trees everywhere, great palms and spiky pandanus and further away almost impenetrable bush, but the chopper hovered over a fairly small semi-circular clearing then came down as fast as was safely possible. They had barely stopped before Stephanie flung off her belt but Boyd Ballinger caught her by the arm; not an easy grip but a forceful deterrent.

'I expect you to know better than haring about madly out there.'

His hand still grasped her arm, his fingers clenched into her soft skin and for a moment that was all that she was aware of. His touch incited a passionate reaction. She wanted to free herself and lash out at his masterful, hard face.

'Marcus could be lying injured some place,' she hissed at him more furiously than she knew. So many old memories and resentments were at work in her and a sharp chemical reaction that she had no time to analyse.

'So we'll find him,' he told her curtly, returning her anger with some of his own. 'That place out there is infested with snakes, pythons, feral animals, grasses that could cut you to pieces. You'll follow me and do *exactly* as you're told. Is that clear?'

A thick lock of her hair had fallen across her forehead and she dashed it away. '*Perfectly* clear, Mr Ballinger.'

'Good.' Only then did he release her. 'There's no use carrying that chip on your shoulder around me.'

That he could say such a thing—think such a thing upset Stephanie unbearably. How she hated him! Had always hated him. He was everything she detested in a man. Tears even stung her eyes and she had to work hard to blink them away. It was like having a painful wound reopened even being in his company.

He was out of the helicopter and coming around to her before her legs even found the strength to jump down.

His silver eyes looked up at her, not soft, but brilliantly hard like melted diamonds. 'You haven't changed much have you from seventeen?'

'I sure as hell have!' She went to ignore his outstretched hand but he settled it all by hauling her out bodily, so she had to clutch at him gasping until she was steady on her feet. One of his arms was still around her and she twisted away.

'All you Ballingers are beyond the pale.'

'There's loyalty!' he jeered. 'My mother was very kind to you. But then in those days you were a very sweet girl.'

'What do you want me to say?' she said hotly. 'Thank you for being kind to a poor little orphan?'

'You are in a vile mood.' He shouldered a pack and reached into the helicopter for his rifle. 'What sort of a man is your ... fiancé—apart from being a fool?'

'Gloriously unlike you!'

He only shook his head. 'Put your hat on.'

'I don't need it.'

'You heard me.' He lifted the cream felt hat out of the helicopter and rammed it on her sumptuous fall of hair.

'Now look here, Mr Ballinger——' she started.

'You look here, Stephanie,' he gripped her wrist, 'you're a big girl now. You sure look one. You've even got yourself a fiancé. Don't you think it's time to throw off that maddening little complex?'

'What complex?' She stared at him, her violet eyes blazing with anger.

'All right, complexes. A whole backload of them. Starting from around age seventeen. That's when the Ballingers became poison.'

'You're crazy!' She tossed her hair back.

'Am I? It's here, right now, the hostility. And this is as far as it goes. You need me, flower-eyes.'

It was so true she swallowed. 'All right.' She couldn't begin to explain to him how it had all happened. Once she had idolised him as much as everyone else. More. Maybe that was it. But that had been a long time ago. A schoolgirl crush on an impossible dream.

'This fiancé of yours,' he was asking curtly, 'he would know how to fend for himself?'

'I guess so. I hope so.' She stared away towards the purple escarpment. 'He knows nothing about the bush.'

'Then why the hell did you let him go?'

'He wanted to go. He's a man!' she protested.

'And he still lost himself.' He smiled his contemptuous, frosty smile, but even then she couldn't help watching the movement of his mouth. The gods had put a lot of effort into Boyd Ballinger. Probably testing how far one could go with a human being.

'I'm afraid,' she said simply.

'Do you love him?'

'I'm engaged to him.'

'I know that. I said do you love him?'

'Of course I love him.'

'I'll bet he can take care of you.' He had picked up a long stick as a staff, testing the grasses.

'And what does that mean?' She was shaking at his tone.

'Security, dear Stephanie. You're big on security. It all comes from being a helpless little girl. Not that you weren't a brave little kid but you had solid ground knocked right out from under you at a very crucial time. Harry and Ellen are good people and they gave you everything they could, but even they couldn't make your world secure and stable. They had—still have—too many troubles themselves.'

'What is it. What's wrong now?' she demanded. He wouldn't stop and she ran to him with a quicksilver grace and grasped his arm. 'Please, Boyd, is there something I should know?'

'Please!' One winged black eyebrow rose

significantly. 'I never dreamed you'd be so polite. Harry and Ellen are always in financial trouble, Stephanie. You know that. They would never have survived this long only for Ellen. She's the manager. Harry just had a dream.'

'But they love the life.'

'They do. They put all their money into Jandra but they've never done more than just barely make it work. Harry is really your typical English gentleman. Dreams alone—an eccentricity if you like—don't carve out a station. It's hard. Fantastically hard. A man has to be tough and strong and fanatically determined.'

'Like the Ballingers?'

'Like the Ballingers,' he agreed. 'Don't knock it, Stephanie, thank God for it. People like the Ballingers opened up this country. Just a handful of families locked into prosperity not only survival. Harry is my friend. No one could help liking him. He's gambled most of his and Ellen's life being a cattleman but he never really was cut out for it. Now they love the life but Ellen has had to put up with a lot of loneliness. She's a great woman, Ellen. Gentle and strong. I think she deserved better.'

They were walking again, Stephanie almost but not quite by his side. 'If you said that to Harry you would kill him.'

'I'm sure Harry has said it to Ellen himself. Your father now might have made it. He was much younger than Harry and he had a lot of extra qualities. One has to be really committed. Total commitment, that's the secret. Harry was more interested in an exotic environment than making a cattle run work. He's enjoyed it all much like an enthusiastic schoolboy on a bush trip while Ellen has agonised how to make ends meet.'

'Yet they saw to it I had a good education,' Stephanie said with deep gratitude. 'How on earth did they manage it. All those years at boarding school, university?'

'I expect Ellen dipped into her handbag,' he dismissed it briefly. 'At least you remained sunny with them.'

'I love them,' she said fiercely. 'You Ballingers may consider you have lots of breeding but let me tell you Ellen came from a far different background than the one she has now.'

'Yes, I've heard that story. Her kinsman the Earl.'

'It's true.'

'I'm not disputing it, you prickly young creature. Harry and Ellen are a case of two very civilised people leading a rather primitive life.'

'And that's what they want.'

'It's cost them, Stephanie.' He stopped walking.

'What is it?' He had stopped so abruptly, that not looking she had slammed into him.

'Be quiet.' He reached around with his arm and thrust her behind him.

'Boyd?' Now her eyes were frantically searching around and ahead. Something had emerged from the trees, swaying the tall, green grasses.

And then they saw it just as it spotted them: a huge, powerfully built boar with great ivory-yellow tusks curving upwards in a savage arc. It was standing perfectly still, then in one stunning moment commenced its charge.

'Ooooh!' Stephanie's low moan died in her throat. She had never felt such fear in a very long time. There were many stories of gorings, for the wild boars were ferocious and only the right bullet could stop their bulk.

The charge was so impetuous it seemed certain one of them would be knocked off their feet and still Boyd didn't get a shot off but waited until the boar was nearly on them, an incredibly ugly thing with a massive head and red hot eyes.

Closer.

Stephanie felt like screaming: 'What are you waiting for?' but in a finger snap of time and a dead-straight aim the boar went down, toppling on its side into the long grass, its mud-caked black coat with a reddish glint in the sun.

'I'd better look around for the rest,' Boyd said abruptly.

'Couldn't you have shot it sooner?' she pressed him, still nursing her fright.

'No way!' was his terse comment. 'It makes no sense you coming with me. Why don't you stay in the chopper?'

'I'm coming to find Marcus.'

'Well he sure as hell isn't mobile.'

The rifle shot had rung out almost deafeningly in the immense silence. The birds were shrieking a protest, the flight of the galahs literally changing colour as they swerved from pearl grey to rose-pink. Even two wallabies sparring play-fully had broken off their boxer pawing and were eyeing the man and his gun with acute wariness.

'We'll have to go the way of least resistance.' Boyd announced his decision. 'Just stay at the back of me. This is home territory for anything that's wild. Including the cattle.'

Ten minutes later Stephanie felt exhausted and soaked through to the skin. Under the great

palms it was languorously hot but in the open the
sun was blinding and obviously a danger.

'Damn it, Stephanie, you can't keep up the
pace.' His expression was a mixture of concern
and hard impatience.

'Oh, go to hell.' She had opened up her shirt as
low as she dared. Yesterday's heat hadn't been
half as deadly as this but then she hadn't been
tracking through dense jungle.

'Little fool!' He pulled her hat off her head and
began to fan her with it. 'You must have gone
soft in the city life.'

The faint breeze was blissful and she arched
her throat back while he fanned her, her deep
mahogany hair curling riotously in the humid
conditions. Briefly she even wondered about
staying put while Boyd went on ahead but she
realised if he left her she would become
desperately uneasy. Strange and beautiful as the
wilderness was, it was far from safe.

'Thank you.' She opened her eyes almost
dazedly, bringing her head up, surprising a
strange glint in his eyes that was gone in seconds.
One thing she was certain about, he had been
studying her very thoroughly.

'Able to go on?'

'Yes.' She tilted her wide-brimmed hat at a
rakish angle, and he immediately adjusted it
because it didn't fully protect her nape.

'You're a great one for taking chances, aren't
you, girl?'

'I just pray God Marcus is in the cool.'

He stayed ahead of her, easing her path and for
a time she was glad of that powerful male
strength. He had a grace of movement that was
peculiar to him, a rippling muscular coordination,

a sleek grace. Like her, he had naturally curling hair, now it clung damply to his handsome skull and clustered into his neck. He wore it longer than Marcus and the thick waves highlighted the impeccably chiselled features. It was entirely reasonable many women had desired him, and she knew he had missed out on precious few of their favours. But he had no real use for women. He was one of those who only regarded a woman as a delicious relaxation. For which they appeared to be immensely grateful.

'Phooey!' Stephanie nearly sobbed the word aloud in bitterness. Sometimes she thought she hated men. Wretched, arrogant unneeding creatures. Always determined to climb to the top. Not letting anything, much less a woman, get in their way. Even the Ballingers suffered in the lean years and Stephanie knew well the Ballinger heir had always worked like a slave. That's what made him so hard.

'All right?' He stopped hacking at an incredibly tenacious vine, forcing the words through his teeth.

'Yes.'

He broke off as his eyes narrowed over her. Her golden-olive skin was deeply flushed and she had several grazes on her arms from cutting and stinging plants. 'I can't find an easier way. I'd say your Marcus has gone down the corridor and perhaps started to explore the tunnels.'

'Then why hasn't he come out?' She sounded almost hysterical, part anxiety and part the throbbing cuts. Boyd too was lacerated but he appeared quite immune.

'I understand how you feel, Stephanie, but just stay with it. We'll find him and he'll be alive.'

His tone challenged her sharply to disbelieve it, but Stephanie felt near to despair. Soon, perhaps very soon they would come on Marcus. It was easy, too easy to surrender up a life in the bush.

At the base of a tall vertical cliff they came to a tranquil pool of apple green water and wordlessly he caught hold of her and pulled her down on the sand. None of his actions shocked her or so she thought until he began to bathe her face and neck. It was unbelievable but he was as tender as if she were a small girl. Blessedly cool runnels of water ran down between her breasts and over her shoulderblades, the thin cotton soaking up the moisture greedily, turning her shirt almost transparent.

'Oh, that's heavenly!' she breathed, and her tongue came out unconsciously to gather in the liquid crystal he was trickling on her face.

'What a hell of a thing to do!' His words exploded with a soft harshness and just as she began to react to such urgency, opening her eyes and straightening her head, he pulled her hard against his chest and with one hand hard at her nape, found her mouth; forcing it open to a conquest that confounded her. She had never received such a kiss in her life, crushing her resistance so she lost herself in a raw, male power.

It was molten, like the sun; scorching her skin and sizzling her blood. She couldn't believe that he would kiss her in this way. Dare to, but a confluence of emotions kept her in his arms, enormous shock and a sexual excitement that was as unwelcome as it was unparalleled.

As abruptly as he took it, he released her mouth, jerking his head back as though repudiating the passion he had unleashed.

'It would be hard to know why you did that,' Stephanie gasped but the glance he gave her now went from sizzling to sardonic.

'Hard for you, maybe. Easy for me. You're a stunning creature. You always were.'

'For God's sake!' she threw him a look of wild reproach, 'I don't think you ever looked at me for longer than two minutes.'

'Believe that and you'll believe anything.'

He couldn't be telling the truth. For ten years he had been at the back of her mind like some undeveloped longing, a man she couldn't possibly have, though Anne Ballinger had attacked her cruelly on what was deepest in her heart. Had she shown her appalling crush on him all those years ago? She still would have sworn that she hadn't. She had hidden her susceptibility for dear life. It was utterly impossible but there was nothing to stop her from weaving daydreams about him. Nearly every woman she knew did that. She had even heard Ellen once say she would be madly in love with him if she were only even ten years younger. Curious how some men were marked out for women's adulation. It wasn't just the physical element though that was blatant enough, it was his natural aura of power, the cast of his mind.

'What's the matter, Stephanie?' he asked sardonically. 'Can't handle it?'

'No.' She threw up her head and her violet eyes blazed. 'You just think you can have everything you like.' The kiss had disturbed her so deeply tears filled her eyes. 'Isn't that what you're trying to prove anyway? What do I care about you and kisses? I'm engaged, don't you remember?'

'Actually I forgot. And so did you.' He was standing looking down at her, stormy eyes, flushed cheeks and heaving breasts, his own eyes frozen lakes and suddenly she was shaken by fury.

She sprang to her feet like a woman in a crazy crisis meaning to slap that pitiless face only he caught her and pinned her in a steel grip, not relinquishing it until she was spent and quivering, her head bowed into his shoulder, the sensitised tips of her breasts grazed by his bush shirt. The lesson of superior power had been a harsh one. She had never felt more impotent in her life, crushed by shame and emotions so intense they were unbearable.

'I'm sorry,' she whispered.

'Maybe I am too.' He lifted her chin probably intending to patch up the situation in any way he could but all of a sudden Stephanie's body became fluid, losing its deep tension. She just looked at him with drowning eyes whether apology or offering, but because of it his arms spasmed across her back and with a muffled exclamation he bent his head again.

Oh, God!

She just let him devour her. All the years' longing realised in a few moments. She forgot Marcus. What the Ballingers had done to her, the impossibility of what was happening now. Not even her own weakness distressed her. She couldn't keep from such a ravishment; proof that the fires of passion she had read about really did exist. Such ecstasy was worth the inevitable burden. Probably it would take a lifetime to eradicate.

It must have been as hard for him to adjust for

he wrenched his head away from such senseless delight. Stephanie was engaged. More. They were searching for the man. Desire was a great leveller cutting the strongest will to pieces.

His handsome face was twisted with self-disgust. 'Put it down to the tangled years,' he told her with a trace of bitterness. 'Time out of mind.'

'It was my fault.'

He considered it then gave a shadow of his beautiful, illuminating smile. 'Truthfully I don't think it was anyone's fault at all. It's just that I'm a man and you're my kind of woman.'

If that were true it was frightening when she had believed otherwise for years. He moved away from her and picked up her hat sending it to her in a little spinning throw. 'Well we didn't get that right did we, flower-eyes? Let's go.'

After that Stephanie was so deeply immersed on what had passed between them she barely noticed the rigours of the remainder of their hike, even the vines that gripped her and he had to release her, the blade-edged grasses that cut into her flesh. A crevice lay ahead of them like a door into the chasmed corridor and he unfastened his pack and thrust it through first.

'What if we don't find him, Boyd?' she asked in a tormented voice.

'We're going to find him.' He reached for her and pulled her through. 'We found the jeep remember? He can't be far off.'

Her blouse was ripped, exposing the lace of her bra and now there was a long scratch running from the back of her ear down towards her collar.

'I should have left you behind,' he said forcefully.

'I had to come. I had to.' Her heart seemed to

be bursting. Exploding inside her with the
violence of her feelings. She was engaged to one
man; not even now knowing his fate, when her
innermost, most secret heart had been enslaved
by another from the very moment her womanhood had come to flower. She didn't understand
it but there was something tortuous about the
guilt.

As they progressed along the narrow corridor
he suddenly spun around and pinned her against
the rocky wall. She couldn't lift her head or her
hands or scarcely breathe. He was so much taller,
broader and he was crushing her, then something,
some creature rushed past them thrashing the
sand and making a spine-chilling reptilian sound.
Still he kept her crushed into him while another
minute passed.

'Did I hurt you?'

'What *was* it?' She let her head fall back,
panting for air.

'Take a look.'

'Oh, hell.' Her legs turned to jelly and she
rested her two arms on his lifted arms, bracing
her against the wall. 'I don't think I've even seen
one so big.' They had startled a monstrous,
chain-mailed perentie, the largest lizard of the
continent and easily two metres long. It was still
racing along the corridor on its ungainly legs, a
reptilian monster from a prehistoric age. 'You
must have eyes like a hawk,' she sighed raggedly.

'It makes for a longer life.'

She was devastated by his smile, a reflection in
his shimmering eyes of liking? Did he like her or
did he only find her sexually attractive? She had
enough inadequacies to gnaw at her.

'There are tracks here,' he observed very

sombrely. 'There among the vines. A man's crepe-soled shoes.'

'Where?' She broke away from him trying to decipher an amazing number of indentations. Mostly marsupials as far as she could see and here the sand was laced with a very pretty vine bearing a wealth of tiny, scarlet flowers.

But Boyd was walking up ahead, deeper into the wild paradise. There were mosses, ferns, vines and orchids, the wild hibiscus and gardenia, the beautiful native grevilleas and dead ahead a beautifully sculptured tunnel, partly hidden by fig and pandanus trees. Even the entrance was curtained by a magnificent glossy green vine with great trumpet shaped flowers almost the colour of Stephanie's eyes.

'Okay, you stay here.' Boyd's arm shot out to urge her back.

'I'm coming with you,' she said stubbornly, her eyes brilliant with distress. 'Marcus must be in there.'

'It seems so.' He turned back to study her face. 'Obviously he's had an accident and it could be bad.'

'So I have to know.'

'Certainly,' he snapped. 'But one accident is enough. You stay back while I go into the cave. Got it?' In his voice was the assurance if she didn't she would cause some unequal confrontation.

'Go ahead, Boyd.' She inclined her head.

A shadow of approval was his only expression then he turned away, straight and tall and intensely alert.

'Probably there are bats.'

'For sure,' he agreed laconically. 'I want you to take shelter over here. Behind me.'

She obeyed him like a child, retreating to a position beneath the scant shade of a pandanus.

'Now.' Boyd swung about, selected a small, polished rock then hurled it into the neck of the dark grey limestone tunnel. Immediately he moved back grasping Stephanie with an authoritative hand and turning her blindly into his side.

The frightened bats screeched out of their velvet retreat, their oddly rustling bodies only feet from Stephanie as she cringed against Boyd Ballinger's protective body. Once long ago a bat had almost caught itself in her hair and she, childlike, had responded with near hysteria. She didn't feel much differently now but after a little while the wild disturbance in the air ceased. His hand travelled down her hair as she kept her head pressed against him. It was like a shuddering excitement that was utterly forbidden. Inside the cave Marcus could be lying. Shame and disgust became a hard ball of pain.

When Boyd left her she drew herself into a tight arc, locking her arms around her knees. 'Damn you, Boyd!' she gasped weakly. 'I didn't want this.'

What if Boyd found the tunnel empty? What if Marcus had already made his way back to the homestead? Impossible. All the evidence pointed to his being in the tunnel. The anxiety was sickening, and images of the injured Marcus crowded her mind.

Just as she thought she would risk Boyd's anger, he emerged from the cave and although Stephanie's mouth opened and closed convulsively no words came out.

'He's here and he's alive,' he called to her. 'Broken leg, slight fever. Bring the pack, Stephanie.'

'Oh, God, oh my God, thank God!' Stephanie sobbed in a prayer.

Boyd slipped away again into the neck of the tunnel and this time Stephanie moved like lightning, collecting Boyd's pack and carrying it into the cave.

After the brilliant sunlight it was like glimmering night but her eyes adjusted before she found the flashlight. Marcus was lying on the ground groaning, tears rolling down his earth-smeared cheeks, his right leg turned at a sickening angle.

'Oh, Marcus, darling!' Her heart smote her forcefully. Only yesterday they had parted in anger, now all resentment was buried.

Boyd had already made him more comfortable now he wanted water.

'I thought no one would ever find me.' Marcus muttered, his voice, normally clear and resonant, a husky whisper.

'Well, it would have taken a lot longer without the helicopter,' Boyd said dryly.

'I can't thank you enough.' His parched mouth moistened, Marcus lay back. 'It was those bloody bats. For some stupid reason I didn't think of bats when I came into the cave.'

'Don't worry, Marcus,' Stephanie responded. 'You can't be expected to know all about the bush.'

'Anyway they came at me in a rush. God, it was horrible. I guess I went sort of mad. I turned and bolted like I was going to be torn to pieces by savage dogs and you know the rest. I hit my head and I broke my leg. At any rate I passed out for a long time.'

Stephanie dusted his face with soft, gentle fingers. 'It's all over now. We'll get you out of here. As soon as you're better we can put an after-dinner story together.'

'But I haven't properly thanked my rescuer here,' Marcus tried to lift his head and frowned. 'You did say who you were but I was too ravaged to catch it.'

'Ballinger,' Boyd repeated.

'Not Steph's bête noir?' Pain and weakness made Marcus light-headed. Normally he would never have made such a faux pas.

'No one else.' Boyd's handsome dark face in the reflection of the torchlight looked monumentally unconcerned.

'Marcus is joking.'

Boyd didn't even glance at her. 'We'll make a splint for that leg then we'll get you out of here. I can't land the chopper any closer. We'll have to manoeuvre the jeep to it. The chopper will be our quickest way in. We can radio ahead to Harry but you'll have to come to Opal. You'll need that leg X-rayed which means I'll have to fly you out to Gascoigne.'

'Thank you.' Marcus, who had been grasping Stephanie's hand, carried it to his mouth. 'All the time I've been here I've been waking-dreaming about you, Steph. Once I must have been a bit delirious because I thought you were with me. Your lovely face . . . you kissed me. Your skin is so cool . . . like silk.'

'Lie still and save your strength,' Boyd Ballinger advised him briefly. 'We have to make it to the jeep yet, but I should be able to carry you.'

'God, man!' Marcus protested weakly, never doubting the other man could toss him over his shoulder. He had never seen any man more superbly fit and Ballinger was several inches taller and more powerfully built. The danger was past and in every respect Marcus felt deeply appreciative.

Stephanie was smoothing his hair and stroking his forehead rhythmically, offering him the comfort he so badly needed. He was sorry now he had been so critical of her aunt and uncle, their unbelievable way of life. Stephanie was a very proud and spirited girl. He had been a fool to sneer at her family. After all it was their life and they seemed to be happy in this god-forsaken wilderness, however savagely beautiful. Something vaguely crossed his mind. His camera. Where was his camera? He had it with him when he first walked into the tunnel, before the air crackled with horrible whirling bodies.

Marcus lifted his head sharply, then passed out.

CHAPTER TWO

DOCTOR STEELE folded his stethoscope, shoved it into the pocket of his white coat and walked out of the door of the emergency room pleased his last patient wasn't going to be with them a long time. Stiff upper lip and that sort of thing was the order of the day in the bush, but this fellow had been complaining from the very moment he had been brought in. It had the staff quite mystified when they had seen stockmen in dreadful pain never cry out. A chap like that would be well advised to stick to city life.

When he saw the two people in the waiting room, Doctor Steele smiled. He was an attractively severe man and not quite as starchy as he looked. 'Nothing much wrong with the patient,' he said. 'The break was a clean one and he has a few rough grazes on his face but he seems rather edgy. I'd like to keep him here until tomorrow. See what his little trauma has done to him. He seemed certain he had come to the Point of No Return.'

'Well, he might have been there a lot longer,' Boyd Ballinger stood up with mock-exhaustion and stretched his lean, wide-shouldered body.

'Thank you, Doctor,' Stephanie said.

'Don't be embarrassed, dear.' Doctor Steele, who knew them both well, laughed. 'Patients behave when things are really serious but some tend to act up as soon as things return to normal. Your friend was just letting go, working off his fright. I'm sure he'll be his old self again by the time he leaves tomorrow.'

'May I see him?' Stephanie asked a little ruefully. She was, in fact, deeply embarrassed by Marcus's behaviour. It had verged on a tantrum. He was acting like a man cut off from civilisation and violently in need of urgent medical attention when Boyd Ballinger had made sure it was easy all the way. He had flown them into Gascoigne in the Super King and an ambulance had been waiting to take Marcus to the hospital. Marcus had been made as comfortable as humanly possible yet now when he had been saved his hazy sweetness had turned to an infuriating burst of self-pity and complaint. She was sure Boyd Ballinger had quelled an almost uncontrollable impulse to knock him out and she knew herself to be deeply mortified. Things were done differently in the bush. Everyone, man, woman and child was so much more stoic. Poor Marcus, she thought. If she hadn't brought him here she doubted if she would ever have known he was so faint-hearted.

When Marcus saw her he grimaced moodily. 'Just look at me! I look like a casualty of war.'

'So aren't you glad you're not in that situation?' Stephanie studied him bracingly. 'The doctor said it was a clean break. It could have been so much worse.'

'Are you sure they know what they're doing here?' Marcus was surprised by her brusqueness.

'Positive, Marcus. All of the staff are highly trained. They have to be. They handle many serious and complicated cases. Yours was plain sailing.'

Marcus gave a great whooping bitter laugh. 'I

feel like a very great fool. Falling over my own legs. I thought Ballinger was looking at me a bit strangely?'

'How are you feeling now?' Stephanie decided to dodge that one. What Boyd Ballinger had been thinking was clear enough.

'Terrible, just terrible.' Marcus lifted his lacerated left hand and stared at it. 'I'll be in this blasted cast for weeks.'

'I know,' Stephanie said more kindly, 'but you really do need a break. All you have to do is sit around and relax.'

'Relax!' Marcus looked up at her in horror. 'You surely don't think I can stay here?'

'Perhaps for the week we planned.'

'Darling,' Marcus shuddered. 'With all due respects to your aunt and uncle it would be a gruelling convalescence. I ask you! They do without the most basic things. I'll have to go home right away or as soon as I'm able and you'll have to come with me.'

'I'm not in the same hurry, Marcus,' Stephanie suddenly sank down in a chair, feeling her headache. 'I see so little of Harry and Ellen these days and they so enjoy the company. I can't tell them I'm leaving. Anyway, I don't want to. I'm entitled to my holiday. God knows it wasn't a simple matter getting here.'

'You can say that again!' Marcus returned bleakly. 'Honestly, darling, this is the end of the world. It might be all right for people like the Ballingers who have the money to make a palace out of the impossible but ordinary people would be quite mad to consider it. I find it quite incredible your aunt and uncle would leave London for a life in this ghastly place. I mean what the devil is a barrister doing in the bush?'

'Adventure,' Stephanie said wryly. 'Harry read a book.'

'My God!' Briefly Marcus covered his eyes. 'And really, you know, Ellen is a lovely woman. It's absolutely mind-boggling the two of them settled down in that nightmarish place.'

'They love it, Marcus,' Stephanie said. 'Their life has brought them very close together. And you seem to have entirely missed the scenery; in the good seasons it's glorious. I don't think I've ever seen a more splendid place than Opal.'

'Well, yes,' Marcus was forced to concede, 'but my dear girl your aunt and uncle are hardly in that class.'

'Most people would think they lead a very comfortable life. You have such set notions about what people need to make them happy. Harry and Ellen are great nature lovers, great readers. They don't need lots of entertainments to keep them sane. And when they do need them they check out for a few weeks always pleased to go home.'

'Just the same it's an unbearably lonely life,' Marcus shuddered involuntarily. 'Ballinger is a very cool sort of chap, isn't he?'

'In what way?'

Marcus shrugged and reached for her hand. 'You two don't get on?'

'Not for many long years.'

'Pity. I thought he might ask us to stay on Opal for a few days. What an extraordinary place! One hardly expects to see a French château in crocodile country. It's the utter incongruity of it all. A place like that in a million acres of nothing.'

'Probably the finest privately owned run in the country and these days the station only represents a small part of their interests.'

'Really?' Despite his discomfort Marcus looked terribly interested.

'A lot of Ballinger money went into Kalka Creek.'

'Good Lord, I never knew that.'

'Something more to make the Ballingers more powerful.' Stephanie said abruptly. 'There they stand, way up there. A family of spectacular accomplishments.'

'Lucky devils!' Marcus sighed. 'A good thing he's not in the city. The women would go mad with adulation. He's a damned arresting man. I didn't think such finely chiselled features could give an impression of so much strength. I think I'd very much like being lord of all I survey.'

A nurse came into the room carrying a hypodermic and Stephanie stood up.

'Is that for me?' Marcus's tone was fearful.

'Just a pin prick.' Nurse Howarth gave him an amused smile. 'Doctor thinks you need a nice, long sleep.'

'Oh, I do!' Marcus was still eyeing her warily. 'All my time in the tunnel was half-dozing nightmares.'

'Well, we'll soon have you on the mend,' Nurse Howarth told him matter-of-factly. 'Like to say good-bye to your fiancée now?'

Stephanie moved to the bed, bent over Marcus very gravely and kissed his forehead.

'Hell, darling!' It was fairly obvious Marcus was disappointed, so Stephanie closed her eyes and kissed his mouth.

When she straightened and looked over her

shoulder Boyd Ballinger and Doctor Steele were standing in the doorway.

'How's it going now?' Boyd Ballinger asked and for a moment Stephanie couldn't accept the total dynamism compared to Marcus's pale inertia.

'I can't thank you enough for all you've done,' Marcus said sincerely. 'I know it's cost you a lot of time and money.'

'People are more important than either.'

Stephanie checked clapping but Marcus looked extremely gratified. 'Frankly I don't know what we would have done without you. When I'm on my feet again I'll really find some way to thank you.'

'Perhaps you'd care to spend a little time on Opal?' Boyd Ballinger suggested. 'Harry and Ellen are getting on in years so they might find it a little difficult while you're in that cast. If I can ease things at all I'd be glad to.'

'That's extremely kind of you,' Marcus said humbly. 'I was just saying to Steph, Opal homestead is magnificent. I'd very much like to see around the place.'

'Well I'll discuss it with Harry and Ellen,' Boyd Ballinger said, casting a brief look at Stephanie's transparent expression.

'What about that injection, Nurse?' Doctor Steele said gruffly. 'Our patient here is a bit pale around the gills. He ought to be glad of a complete rest.'

'That was a marvellous idea of yours,' Stephanie told Boyd Ballinger as they left the hospital.

'Sure.'

'You don't seem to have considered I mightn't like it very much?'

'Don't worry, I've invited you.' He took her arm in a detaining grip as a stationwagon surged into view.

'You can hardly suppose I would want to go to Opal?'

'Why not, Stephanie?' his silver eyes crackled.

'I want nothing more than to be with Harry and Ellen.'

'Not your fiancé?' he asked jeeringly. 'You don't love him so you might as well tell me how he fits in?'

'I do love him.'

'Sorry, flower-eyes.'

'He's not used to this environment. He's behaving rather differently away from home.' He still held her arm and she felt herself trembling.

'I'll bet that's taken the shine off things faster than anything.'

'I wish you wouldn't interfere in what doesn't concern you.'

'Right.' He dropped his arm. 'I'll leave you here.'

Suddenly she felt so helpless she lifted her hands to her temples in a gesture of despair. She had come out here with Marcus. Someone she wanted to love, now she felt their whole relationship had been damaged irrepairably.

'It's all right, Stephanie.' He put his hands on her shoulders. 'Where does it hurt, the head, the heart, or both?'

She lifted her head very slowly. 'I think I'd like a cup of tea.'

'Then we'll get you one. Why didn't you drink the tea the nurse brought you?'

'I was too worried about Marcus.'

'Marcus will be fine.' He adopted a tone of cool

professionalism. 'Let's cross the street to the hotel. It's hours since you've eaten anything. You're probably hungry.'

'Yes,' she agreed shakily. 'How long before you get away?'

'I want to be back on Opal before nightfall.'

'But, Boyd——'

There was a glimmer of mocking sympathy in his eyes. 'I suppose you think I should deliver you home tonight?'

'I hate to impose on you.' Her heart had given a fearful jolt.

'No imposition at all,' he said brusquely. 'You've always been welcome on Opal whether you can handle it or not.'

She waited until they crossed the street before she took a breath. 'On the other hand I could stay at the hotel. Wait for Marcus.'

'And what are you going to do for money?'

'You can speak to them.'

'No, I won't,' he said, his voice deep and smooth. 'I want to settle this little matter why you won't set foot in my home.'

'We don't have an awful lot in common.'

'I was thinking a little more than you appear to have with your fiancé.'

'I told you, you don't really know him.'

He led her up the stairs of the very decorative hotel, three-storeyed and enveloped in white wrought-iron lacework. 'You don't have to be so damned defensive. Tell me, is he always so poor-spirited?'

'Would you believe he runs a very successful business?'

'I thought being penniless might affect your decision.'

Anger overrode every other emotion. She stopped dead in her tracks, pulling away from him violently. 'I absolutely detest you, Boyd Ballinger.'

'That's what I like about you,' he returned suavely, watching the wild apricot colour surge along her delicate high cheekbones. 'God knows I've endured enough women telling me how much they love me.'

'They must have been masochists.'

'A few of them,' he said. 'Listen, Stephanie, why don't we continue this conversation out of the sun? You're shaking and your skin is flushed.'

'You'd make anyone furious,' she said. 'Just because I happen to admire ambition in a man.'

'Plus a very safe harbour.' He threw his arm around her and gripped her for a moment. 'You know, you really should have been a redhead.'

'Let me go, damn you, Boyd,' she hissed, very quietly.

'I will now.' He nodded pleasantly at a couple who had started their descent of the stairs. 'Later I might give you a little something to remember me by.'

They flew into Opal as the sun was going down and Stephanie looked out the window at the majesty of the red plains blanketed in flowers. Opal occupied an enormous oval-shaped valley bordered on two sides by ranges with fantastic vertical cliffs. No great station of the tropical North was one half so impressive and the region abounded in dramatic, natural spectacles; magnificent wild vistas, volcanic rock formations, gorges and waterfalls, water-sculptured grottoes, lush oases where the luxuriant tropical growth was exquisite and away in the distance, by contrast, eerie stony hills where it was impossible to get the black man to go. The Stone Country was supposed to be inhabited by powerful spirits and it was guarded along the perimeter by strange whitish spires that at a distance looked for all the world like an army. Opal was a kingdom and the Ballinger right to power undisputed. The history of the family was the history of the island continent. No one else but magnificently brave men could have hoped to found and hold onto a great pastoral dynasty. And the station remained intact and in the possession of the one family which added immeasurably to its considerable mystique. It was, as Stephanie only too clearly realised, one of the great pastoral holdings of the world and an ever-present reminder ordinary people didn't often make it into the ranks of the élite.

'This is it, Stephanie, we're in.'

They were taxiing now towards the great silver hangar. It had been a perfect touch-down after a smooth, non-eventful flight. Several station hands were in attendance and Stephanie stifled her dismay as she recognised the fair-haired woman who sat behind the wheel of the jeep parked outside the office.

Anne Ballinger.

For moments Stephanie retreated into the ghastly past when that cold and beautiful woman had heaped every ugly name she could think of on her hapless, unsuspecting head. My God, who else could have called a totally innocent young girl a 'sex-starved slut'?

'I see your *aunt* is here to welcome you,' she said ironically. Anne Ballinger, in fact, was about the same age as Boyd, thirty-two, thirty-three, which made her twenty years her husband's junior. Years ago people had said she married him for his money. Ralph Ballinger was still a handsome man but Anne with her looks and good family name might have aspired to the Ballinger heir.

But Boyd had ignored her. Others said she had married Boyd's uncle just to be around, that she never would cure herself of a hopeless passion, but in those early days the young Stephanie had liked to think she really did love her husband. Anne was Ralph Ballinger's second wife. His first wife, Margaret, had died with their daughter in a flash flood and for many years after Ralph Ballinger had acted like a man who knew happiness was forever out of his reach.

As Stephanie walked towards the jeep she could see that the older woman's light green eyes were as cold and bleak as ever.

'Why . . . Miss Sinclair.' She hesitated over the name.

'Isn't that rather formal,' Boyd intervened. 'We've known Stephanie a long time.'

'Sorry—Stephanie.' The thin mouth smiled. 'Couldn't make it back to Jandra?'

'Unfortunately no.' Stephanie looked back steadily, her expression very cool and composed. This too was a pleasure because now she was discovering light years had past. Without vanity she knew that she was beautiful and she could hold her own in any company. Harry and Ellen had sacrificed a great deal to give her a first-class education and if those two things didn't give her confidence, now she knew Boyd Ballinger found her physically desirable.

'Aren't you going to ask how the patient is,' Boyd challenged her squarely.

'Of course I am, darling.' With brittle grace she moved over so he could drive. 'Indeed I am. How *is* your fiancé . . . Stephanie?'

'Feeling very sorry for himself. One way and another it's been quite a day.'

'Strange, you don't look tired.' Anne Ballinger darted her a sudden, suspicious look over her shoulder.

'Boyd made sure I had a good lunch.'

'Really, where?' Anne laughed to cover her disapproval.

'The local pub,' Boyd drawled laconically.

'I'll bet everyone wishes you'd be so kind to them.'

'There can't be a kinder man alive,' Stephanie confirmed sweetly. They were picking up speed and her long hair streamed behind her in the cooling, evening breeze. She hates me as much as she ever did, Stephanie thought. It was absurd really. Anyone would think she had been part of their lives instead of a marginal figure.

Minutes later they were approaching the house and Stephanie forgot about Anne Ballinger. A sense of heritage she didn't even know she possessed came at her in a rush.

'Pull up, Boyd,' she exclaimed, leaning forward to touch his shoulder and he nodded and did so immediately as though exactly tuned into her wavelength.

'I never thought I'd be heart sick, homesick for Opal,' she said wonderingly.

'Honestly, Miss Sinclair,' Anne Ballinger laughed uproariously and swung around to face her.

'It must be unique in all the world.'

'A different world,' Boyd said. He too was half

turned, looking from Stephanie's glowing face and wildly tumbled hair to the great stone mansion that completely dominated that remote plain. Réné Ballinger, who had built it, had been born in Scotland of a French mother, and the design of Opal was reminiscent of a particular château that had bewitched him as a child. The sophisticated roof form was there, the pepper pot towers at either end of the front façade but the central wing was protected by broad verandahs supported by pairs of lofty stone pillars forming a magnificent colonnade. It was a château of the new world and it had been far more difficult to erect than the great château from which it took its inspiration.

It was impossible not to romanticise Opal, just as it was impossible not to romanticise each successive custodian.

'Seen enough?' Anne Ballinger inquired, her ash-blonde hair a light halo around her face. She wore it, as always, in a classic pageboy and it suited her cool, fine-boned features.

'No hurry,' Boyd answered. His arm was lying along the back of the seat and Anne brought her hand up and touched it. She had never allowed her skin to tan and she looked lily pale against his polished bronze.

'Darling,' she said beguilingly, 'aren't you dying for a drink?'

He shook his head, his silver eyes resting briefly on her upturned face. 'This is the wrong country to get the taste for it.'

'Oh, come on,' she said huskily, though she flushed 'I've never seen anyone who could drink you under the table.'

'Now and again when there's not much harm done.'

It was a curious exchange and Stephanie withdrew from it. Funny how she had never noticed how Anne Ballinger looked at Boyd. The quality of the glances, the tone of her voice. She had just taken it for granted a woman couldn't possibly marry one man and love another. Now as she shaded her eyes looking towards the magnificent manicured acres of Opal's home gardens she made a rapid reappraisal. Anne Ballinger couldn't keep her eyes off him, her hand from touching his skin. It was as clear a case of forbidden passion as Stephanie had ever seen. Incredible! She even found herself sighing. It even explained in part why the older woman had attacked her. She knew now that although Boyd had mostly teased her in the manner of a self-assured adult to a teenager, he had occasionally told her that one day she was 'going to break a lot of hearts'. Clearly it was a compliment of a sort, certainly the biggest she remembered, because his attitude had always been nonchalant, mocking, but Anne Ballinger had taken it to heart. She had a vast sense of property, possession and if she hadn't been able to secure Boyd Ballinger for herself, no other woman would get her blessing.

Boyd parked the jeep right at the base of the broad rise of steps. 'Cath's home,' he told Stephanie, who was standing looking rather apprehensively at the open doorway.

Now her face changed, lighting up in an enchanting smile. 'Cath! How lovely!'

'So you can smile sometimes.'

She ignored him, feeling relief sweep through her veins. 'You never told me Cath was here.'

'Cath and heir.' He put his hand on her shoulder and led her up to the stairs with lithe grace.

'Why—that's marvellous. Ellen told me Cath had a son. Peter, isn't it?'

'That's it.' He laughed indulgently. 'The cutest little kid I know.'

'So you're an uncle?' Anne Ballinger had gone ahead of them and Stephanie paused with her hand on the stone balustrade.

'And I like it.'

'Good. You'll certainly be required to produce a son.'

'Are you trying to sell me on marriage, Stephanie?' His eyes were mocking and bright silver.

'I guess you'll have to think about it sometime.'

'No problem, flower-eyes. For different reasons I'll have quite a few to choose from.'

'So you will,' her smile was thin. 'There's always some woman perfectly willing to give up everything to serve.'

'Are you insulting me, Stephanie, on my doorstep?'

'I'm trying to.'

'Why?' He put out a hand so she had to hold to her position pressed back against the balustrade.

'To be honest, I don't like you. Remember?'

'Then don't change,' he said scoffingly. 'Your kisses are absolutely fatal.'

She would have liked to whip out a crushing retort but the sexual excitement that had passed between them came flooding back. 'I do believe you're blushing, Stephanie?' he laughed softly and moved away.

'I do have an awfully quick temper.'

'The mark they tell me of a very passionate woman.'

When Boyd's sister, Catherine, heard that Stephanie had arrived, she went running down the great staircase.

'Stephanie!' She threw out her arms. 'You look so beautiful . . . beautiful!'

'Cathy, I had no idea you were going to be here.' Smiling Stephanie clutched Boyd's sister, captivated as ever by Catherine's intense charm. Five years now since she had seen her but Cathy never seemed to change. She had always laughed and chatted almost nonstop, a startling changeling in the Ballinger family for she had quite missed out on the stunning, Ballinger good looks and the distinctive manner. She wasn't even impressively tall but of all things a petite redhead with a very pleasing open face but no pretentions to the family beauty. Cath's elder sister, Julia, was that, Boyd's female counterpart, a high-powered beauty who had bypassed even the most superficial friendship with the young Stephanie. Julia, too, was married. Absolutely the right person, but rumour had it she was no more in love with her immensely wealthy husband than Anne Ballinger was with hers. Both had made the same gesture—putting their heads before their hearts.

Cathy was a softer, warmer more caring person altogether. And yet because there scarcely seemed any other way for a Ballinger, she had married extremely well; but of course a man who cared for her as deeply as she cared for him. Stephanie had met Jim Gower many times and she had thought from the beginning he was a fantastic match for Cathy.

After that the two girls seemed to go off together as though they had so much to talk about and so little time to do it. Peter was having a long nap and Cathy chose Stephanie's room, the two of them making up the huge, four-poster bed exchanging information at an almost dizzying rate.

'And you really love him?'

'Mmm, yes.'

'That's a funny answer.' Now that she had made the bed, Cathy threw herself back on it. 'Too guarded by half when you're the most feeling person. The most vivid girl I've known.'

'I was sure I loved him,' Stephanie finished opening back the shutters on the French doors then sat down on a Louis-style daybed heaped with softly shimmering satin cushions.

'But?' Cathy rolled over and held her head in her hands. Her essential sweetness was her mother's and she did have a faint look of that beautiful woman; something about the expression and the shining candour of her gaze.

'He's just someone else up here.'

'I never thought you could fall in love with anyone else but Boyd,' Cathy said amazingly.

'Cathy!' Stephanie felt panic run like ice through her veins.

'Don't look so shocked, Steph. Gosh, there's nothing I'd want more.'

'But Boyd!' Stephanie passed her hand before her eyes. 'I've never been anything to Boyd. It's the utmost fantasy.'

'So he was much older than you then. He isn't now. Ten years. I think that's just the right difference. Besides, as cruel as it may seem, a man can give a woman ten years anyday. I worry about it all the time. I'm six weeks older than Jim.'

'I can't imagine you'll look anything else but youthful. Even when you're eighty,' Stephanie smiled.

'I sure hope so.' Cathy studied Stephanie's face. 'I'm sorry, love. Have I shocked you?'

'Yes, a little. I hope to God you've never mentioned any of this to Boyd.'

'Good Lord, no. I dread Boyd marrying the wrong woman. I love him so much it hurts.'

'And why should he marry the wrong woman?' Stephanie asked.

'It's amazing the things that happen. Look at Julia! The most beautiful, imperious creature and she's gone as hard as nails.'

'Has she?'

Cathy nodded her red-gold head. 'Mamma thinks when she left here she left all her tender feelings behind. She's very much the brilliant hostess now. Another one of Eric's possessions. And she's so clever really and so much more sensitive than she makes out. You think about the sort of women who fall in love with Boyd.'

'Spare me. It would take too much time.'

'Some of them I've loathed. Types like Anne. Power-crazy. Boy, wouldn't she love to be the chatelaine here! Anne's like a thorn in my mind especially when I see her trying to make up to Boyd. It's so embarrassing. How Uncle Ralph fails to see it I don't know, or maybe there's no love there either. Poor Uncle Ralph! His life was shattered years ago.'

'Anne doesn't want a family?'

'It doesn't seem like it.' Cathy trailed her hand across the splendid rose silk coverlet. 'I wish you'd tell me what went wrong between you and Anne.'

'When is this, Cathy?' Stephanie's violet eyes widened.

'Oh, I know she offended you. She offends me and I'm Boyd's sister. She's jealous of anyone he cares about.'

'I've had very little to do with Anne at all.' Stephanie let her head fall back, staring up at the beautifully decorated plaster ceiling. It was ivory, picked out in almond and gold. 'I do know she doesn't like me.'

'I'll say! She drove you away from here. I know she did. It could never have happened only Mamma remarried and went away. Mamma was your friend. She'd have given Anne a good setting-down.'

'No, no, nothing happened, Cath,' Stephanie said quietly. 'You're just dreaming when you think Boyd could have any interest in me. Actually, we've always been faintly hostile.'

'Do you think I wouldn't know if my brother liked you?' Cathy countered. 'Boyd was always attracted to you but the idea of being attracted to a kid made him angry. Remember my twenty-first birthday party?'

'Just vaguely.' Stephanie laughed. Would she ever manage to forget it?

'I was supposed to be the birthday girl yet you looked so beautiful. Ellen managed to get a dress that was the exact colour of your eyes. What does Boyd call you? Flower-eyes. I think you shocked him that night. Knowing you were a woman. Before that he used to focus a bit too much on your being a mere schoolgirl. Even Julia thought you looked marvellous. Praise indeed. Julia has wonderful looks but she hasn't got your sort of vitality. You light up.'

'And you don't?' Stephanie asked. 'Julia may look absolutely perfect but I know which sister I love.'

'That's wonderful!' Cathy smiled. 'Funny how we've always had this rapport. Mamma still asks about you.'

'She was always very kind to me.'

'Nothing changes, does it?' Cathy sighed. 'If Boyd said Marcus could come here why don't you let him?' The hazel eyes grew serious. 'You're not making a marriage of convenience, are you, Steph?'

'Well I'm not consumed with passion,' Stephanie said in a curious way. 'I sound disloyal to Marcus but my feelings have changed. He's a different person away from the city and its glitter. He's furious this has happened to him.'

'Goodness, shouldn't he be thankful? It could have been so much worse.'

'We had an argument,' Stephanie said abruptly. 'That's why he went off on his own. Had I been with him he would never have had his accident.'

'And what was the argument about?' Cathy sat up with a jerk.

'Oh, I think being in the bush was getting him down. Then some plant was making him sneeze. Harry and Ellen read him at once as being a city-slicker.'

'And what does Ellen think? After all, Ellen is someone special. She can read people like a book.'

'I guess they're both disappointed,' Stephanie said. 'I scarcely recognise Marcus myself up here. He's at war with the environment. At work he's someone quite different. So clever and competent and of course he's good looking with an air of

cultivation. He was the one who became serious
first. Even when you're cool to them men seem
to find you attractive. Then he was my boss
and I suppose I was flattered. Marcus can be
excellent company and he's determined on
success. I admired him. Admire him. I don't
know whether it's really fair to judge him off
his home ground.'

'Would you accept that Boyd could look
different in the city?' Cathy asked simply.

'You mean Ballinger, by God,' Stephanie
exclaimed a trifle harshly. 'Boyd is like Julia.
They're the brilliant ones wherever they are.'

'You know you puzzle me, Steph,' Cathy said.
'I'd swear my brother has hurt you only I know
better.'

'I told you, Cathy, we share a characteristic
hostility, antagonism, if you like.'

'My dear!' Cathy raised reddish-brown eye-
brows at her, 'antagonism is probably the prelude
to love.'

'Sorry!' Stephanie laughed aloud. 'Your
brother will marry some elegant, compelling
creature from his own fastidious circle and I will
return to the city. Undoubtedly with my fiancé.
We get along a whole lot better there.'

'Then I've got to meet him,' Cathy declared.
'Now my little man has been sleeping a long time.
I think I'll wake him up. I can't wait for you to
see him. He's gorgeous! Not like me.' Cathy
smiled her smile of great sweetness. 'He's the
image of his Daddy.'

'Undoubtedly you'll have one with red hair.'
Stephanie stood up rather dreamily and held out
her hand. 'You don't know how lucky you are,
Cathy. I think it would be marvellous to have a

loving family around me, a wonderful husband and an adorable little son.'

'You've felt it all deeply, haven't you?' Cathy said. 'We all had the greatest admiration for you, you were so brave.'

'I had to be.' Stephanie's eyes held a reflection of the old agony, the dreadful years when she had mourned her mother and father with a helpless pain. 'I don't know what I would ever have done without Harry and Ellen. They tried so hard to surround me with love. It was terrible for Harry too. He was the one who talked Daddy into coming to Australia.'

'Ah,' Cathy said softly, under her breath. 'I really don't know why such terrible things happen. You losing your parents, Uncle Ralph losing his wife and child. When they brought my father in, Mamma's screams filled the house. One reason she can't stay here. She can't, you know. Wonderful as Opal is, Mamma always says it mocks her. I'd say we're all damned lucky Boyd came out of the heroic mould. Mark and Uncle Ralph just walk in his shadow. Sometimes I think Mark will never come to terms with having a brother like Boyd though he really worships him.'

'Mark will find himself,' Stephanie said. 'Ellen keeps me up with all the family news. Isn't there a new girl in his life?'

'Paula Armstrong,' Cathy jabbed a hand through her short curls. 'She's very nice. I don't think you ever met her. She's been three years in London, enjoying it very much.'

'I think I did meet her. Once, a long time ago. Blonde, blue eyes?'

'I think that would have been Ruth, her elder

sister.' Both girls walked to the door. 'When do you have to go home, Steph?'

'Well—' Stephanie took a deep breath. 'We only had two weeks and nearly a week of that has gone.'

'You've got to stay with us.'

'I can't leave Harry and Ellen, Cath.'

'Maybe for a few days?' Cathy pleaded. 'No one even told me you were here.'

'No one knew. I don't advertise my arrival. I didn't even want Harry to call Boyd, but thank God he did.'

'Are you sure you don't want to tell me what started it all?' Cathy looked earnestly into Stephanie's face. 'You dropped us years ago. Just like that. I know you thought you had to. We were all so taken with you.'

'You mean you and your mother,' Stephanie observed mildly.

'I've always felt it was something Anne said to you. Something deliberate to cripple our friendship.'

'Instead of which,' Stephanie smiled, 'we've taken up where we left off. Come and show me this wonderful son of yours, then I'm going to lie in the bath for an hour. I feel really frazzled.'

'I'll find something for you to wear to dinner,' Cathy said soothingly. 'There's a whole wardrobe of Julia's things. She told me to give everything away. There's such a thing as being too damned self-indulgent. A lot of it she's never even worn and I'm too ordinary let alone short to wear them.'

'I can wear the things I have on, Cath,' Stephanie said.

But Cathy wouldn't hear of it. 'No,' she said

firmly, 'I want you to look beautiful. I've been waiting for you to come back here and look beautiful for a long time.'

CHAPTER THREE

SHE met Mark in the library and he stared at her for a moment as though she were some mysterious stranger. She could see the wonderment in his eyes, the arrested movement of his hand, his drink half-way to his mouth.

'Mark, how nice to see you.' Stephanie came on gracefully and still he stood immobilised. 'It's Stephanie, of course.' She extended her hand.

'Stephanie,' he repeated, his temporary enslavement over. 'Forgive me if I'm gawking. You've finally grown up and you look fabulous!'

A handshake didn't seem to be meaningful enough so Stephanie offered her cheek. He looks like Boyd she thought, tall, darkly handsome, the sterling silver eyes, all there yet with only a fraction of Boyd's impact. She couldn't help thinking it was unfair and how much damage it could do to the weaker personality.

But Mark was not going to be easily fobbed off with her cheek. Her sudden appearance had unnerved him, bringing back a whole host of memories. She had always been a very pretty girl with that rich crown of hair and those beautiful blue eyes but a few years had wrought an enormous refinement. Now each feature was distinctly defined, the always slender body pared to perfection. She was infinitely more beautiful and the soft, vulnerable look had been replaced by an expression of confident, conscious charm.

Stephanie Sinclair, the hapless little orphan, had grown up.

'Why you're beautiful,' he said, proceeding to make contact with her mouth.

'I'm glad you think so.' With one gentle hand against his chest she held him off. A kiss from Mark Ballinger wasn't what she wanted at all.

'And to think you're engaged?' He slid his arm lightly around her waist. Her skin was a gleaming, pale gold, lending an exotic quality to those extraordinary violet eyes. Once the circumstances of her life had made her very vulnerable. He wondered if that might still apply now.

'So you've met? That's fine.' A voice said from the doorway and instantly Mark dropped his arm.

'Want me to pour you a drink, Boyd?'

'Thank you. I wouldn't really mind. Scotch, a little water. What about you, Stephanie?'

Now she had to look at him. She couldn't go on putting it off. 'A very dry sherry, if you have one.'

'Mark.' He gave his brother an unconsciously commanding nod.

'I might have to go down to the cellar and bring that one up,' Mark said with a grin. 'We've got absolutely everything else.'

'Sherry, Mark,' Boyd said.

'I'll get it right now.' Mark looked at Stephanie and winked. 'You just sit down and wait. On the other hand you could come down to the cellar with me?'

'We'll wait,' Boyd confirmed. 'So long as you're going bring back a couple of bottles of Bollinger and ask Martha to ice them.'

'Will do.' Mark looked quickly over at Stephanie. 'I guess this is some sort of a celebration. It's a few years now since Stephanie has been inside the house.'

'None of us can ignore that,' Boyd murmured very dryly after his brother had gone. 'Why have you settled yourself so far away from me?'

'You mean now?' Stephanie wondered now if she had only dreamed the intervening years.

He picked up his drink and followed her across the splendidly proportioned, traditionally furnished room.

'I knew you had to have a chance at seeing the rest of the world before.' His silver eyes touched on her face, very delicately and expertly made-up, travelled over the white pure silk dress, Grecian inspired to show off a beautiful body, along her long lovely legs to the palest pink leather court shoes Cathy had found for her. 'I think you seduced Mark on the spot.'

'What nonsense!' she said gently.

'In every respect, Stephanie, you've grown up.'

'I must have. I've lost my fear of you.'

'Substitute a girlish awe.'

'That too.' The air seemed to be vibrating with a wealth of unspoken things, the knowledge of their explosive lovemaking which neither could find an excuse for, Mark's irresistible urge to try to prove himself some kind of a match for his brother, the conceivable reasons for Stephanie's alienation from the family.

'I wonder how Marcus is now?' It seemed incredible but she couldn't fully visualise his face.

'I'll get Don Morris to fly him back tomorrow. I can't afford the time.'

'We've put you to a great deal of trouble.'

'That's okay, Stephanie,' his voice was low and

amused. 'There's not much I wouldn't do for you.'

'You wouldn't take me home.' It was a dream to have him so near her, a kind of a smouldering joy and a torment.

'As a matter of fact,' he gave her the smile that so lit his face, 'Harry and Ellen are very pleased you're here. They've wanted it for a long time.'

'Wanted what?' she asked with soft tension.

'Don't get disturbed, Stephanie,' he looked her full in the eyes. 'I only meant we all knew something had gone wrong. Overnight you were almost another person.'

'I felt another person, Boyd. I am.'

'And what is it about your Marcus you want?'

'The kind of life he's offering me.'

'I was afraid you were going to say that.'

'You're always the same, Boyd, aren't you? You never change.'

'I'm the same as I always was about you.' He looked towards the door then stood up as Anne Ballinger swept in from the hallway as though terrified to see them alone.

'This looks nice and cosy.'

'Perfect,' Boyd said. 'Just like the old days.'

'I see you've been invading Julia's wardrobe?' Anne glanced pointedly at Stephanie's dress.

'Yes. I picked the best thing I could find.'

'Actually *I* picked it all out,' Cathy, looking sweet and mischievous, stood inside the doorway wrinkling her small, upturned nose at Anne Ballinger's comment. 'Steph dressed up to please me. Isn't she beautiful?'

'Too damned beautiful,' Boyd observed, his sculptured mouth faintly twisted. 'For that matter, where's Mark now?'

'So you've seen Mark?' Cathy smiled and went to perch on the arm of her brother's chair.

'Yes.' As she turned her head Stephanie's brilliant eyes flashed. 'I don't think I fitted the old image he had in his mind.'

'My God, no!' Anne Ballinger laughed. 'You were such a mouse.'

'*Mouse!*' Cathy gave a shout of scornful laughter 'It's a wonder that didn't choke you, Anne. Steph's about as mousy as Brooke Shields.'

'Who's Brooke Shields?' Anne asked blandly. 'I only meant . . .'

'We know what you meant,' Boyd intervened. 'Isn't Ralph coming down to dinner?'

'Yes,' Anne answered and her thin face flushed. As she looked at Boyd something glimmered nakedly in her pale, imperious face and Stephanie felt a thrust of pity. Anne had made her choice but it had not been part of her plan. It was a mistake for her to continue living here feeling as she did about a man who was not her husband. She ought to move right away. It was terribly unhealthy.

Mark rejoined them and a short time later, Ralph Ballinger. He was a very distinguished looking, gentlemanly man but in quiet moments his face bore an expression of unutterable loneliness. Moreover he seemed oblivious to his wife's behaviour, treating her with the same remote charm he extended to all women. He seemed not at all eager for her special attention, simply joined in like an urbane guest at a house party. If his wife were in love with his nephew, Ralph Ballinger for one didn't seem to care a scrap.

It was, Stephanie considered, truly weird, though she realised still water often tended to run deep. He was even looking a little frail against the obvious health and strength of his nephews. It persuaded her to be very gentle with him and gradually their conversation became easier and less formal.

Dinner was served in the magnificent, two-storied, glass-enclosed conservatory rather than in the formal dining room which was far too sumptuous a setting for every day. As far as Stephanie was concerned it was perfect. Stars blossomed outside while inside was the most glorious profusion of plants, hanging, soaring, climbing, enormous ferns and peace lilies, every conceivable philodenron in all their tropical glory, long hanging arches of native orchids, white and gold and pink, the spectacular blue passion flower, the jasmines and dracaena, a host of flowering bromeliads and anthurium, mixed plantings in great umbrella-shaped containers and baskets of uncommonly large hydrangea kept since Louise Ballinger's time because she loved and missed the plant so much. Only the gardenias were kept outside because in the humid heat their perfume was overpowering.

There was an immeasurable difference in how Stephanie felt now as compared to then. She was even utterly unaffected by Anne Ballinger's barbed little comments which finally faltered to a cold and sullen silence. The rest of the family were relaxed, obviously striving to regain the old carefree footing and in the process favouring Anne with the occasional quelling look of condemnation. They had absolutely no idea of what had passed between Stephanie and Anne

Ballinger but they still saw the need to defend
Stephanie.

'You must be awfully good at your job, Steph,'
Cathy now said. Stephanie had been telling them
about a fashion account she had captured which
had brought her directly to Marcus's notice.

'Oh, I enjoy it,' she smiled, 'though it's a rather
frantic way of life. So much competition. I took
courses in just about everything art, sociology,
psychology, business management, journalism. It
was difficult to cram all that study in.'

'It would have been more difficult still without
Boyd.' Anne Ballinger's voice came out as sharp
and splintery as glass.

'I beg your pardon?' Stephanie's stomach
lurched so badly she sat forward with her hands
clenched around the arms of her rattan chair.

'She means I was praying for you, Stephanie, I
suppose,' Boyd answered at once and signalled to
Lan Ying, their Chinese houseboy, that they were
ready for coffee.

'I knew absolutely you were going to be a
success.' Cathy threw her uncle's wife a look of
wild reproach.

'Can we go back a bit?' Stephanie touched her
head. It couldn't be. It was impossible.

'It takes money to get through university, my
dear,' Anne's fair face shone with malice.

So it *was* true.

In an instant all Stephanie's protective confidence fell from her. It was as if she had been
stripped naked in public. 'I'm sorry,' she said
vaguely and stood up.

'*Stephy!*' Catherine put her hands to her face
as though she were about to cry but Stephanie
gave a funny little moan under her breath and

without looking right or left moved swiftly out into the garden beneath the eternally blossoming stars. She had no idea where she was going but it had all come back, the bewilderment and the pain, the crushing sense of humiliation. She had wondered for years how Harry and Ellen had found the money to support her when they had taken such a beating in the floods of the late 70s. Of course Harry had always told her they could afford it and Ellen had been there to back him, both of them so proud of her high level of achievement.

Her whole body was suffused with the heat of humiliation.

'Stephanie!'

She heard Boyd's voice call to her, as hard and authoritative as the crack of a whip. Her skin was burning and her eyes were half blinded by tears. She drew back against a flowering oleander, then when he turned away she ran, not stopping, thinking pain was the inevitable consequence of having anything to do with the Ballingers. How could Harry and Ellen ever have found the money after a period of such adversity? She was heart sick with her own simple-mindedness.

If only it had been anyone else but Boyd! She could have killed him easily at that moment for making her so accountable to him. There was a summer house in the walled garden, almost a temple with a tiled roof and seven marble columns. Boyd's grandmother had had it erected to compliment the classic formality of that section of the garden. Once it had been Stephanie's favourite spot and its isolation drew her now. She knew what she had to do. She had to get away from the Ballingers before they destroyed her.

'Oh, Marcus where are you?' she moaned softly. But Marcus was far away and already her mind and body were rejecting him. The wilderness had rendered him impotent, stripping him of all strength and glamour. She had known all along she never really loved him. Neither had she ever felt the trembling urgency of being in love. Marcus had represented a secure future, the two of them pursuing a trouble free world.

There was no such thing. No place on the road there wasn't pain. She had become engaged to Marcus for the worst possible reasons, placing security and comfort above the terrible menace of loving. Once she had been frightened everything she loved would be taken from her. She had nearly gone insane when Ellen had taken very ill. It was a reaction to the terror of her childhood, the thought of being ravished by emotion that could tear one apart.

She ran so far and so fast on her high heels her heart was pumping in agitation and she almost fell down on the circular bench, her mind searching frenziedly for a way out. She had very little money. In her job she was expected to dress beautifully and quality clothes were expensive to say nothing of accessories. She had her car and a little over fifteen hundred dollars in the bank. When she had first started work she sent a monthly cheque to Harry and Ellen, some small token of gratitude for all they had done for her but they had refused to touch them. She felt suffocated by a choking grief. If only they had told her! What did she care about university . . . but she had cared, cared terribly. It was easy to study when one was far from home and Harry and Ellen were always so proud of her.

'You really should keep up with your painting!' Ellen often told her. 'You're a lot better than you think.'

She had heard it often enough at art classes but the big thing was earning money. Her creative ability with words was another talent. But the money for her education had come straight from Boyd Ballinger. The mortification was so deep she thought it would be with her all her life.

Of course he found her, his tall figure silhouetted against the night sky. 'What the hell is all this about?' he asked jaggedly.

'Don't lie to me, Boyd.' Her voice came out in an impassioned sob.

'Lying is not my style,' he returned severely, 'But running is yours.'

'To hell with you!' she stood up to face him. 'I've never wanted anything from you, Boyd. Your admittance, your acceptance, your money, your anything!'

'I understand that, Stephanie,' he answered, shocking her now with the living aura of power, a hard, male presence that mocked her feminine fragility. 'In a sense that's what all this conflict is about. I think you're terrified you might come to love me.'

'You're insane!'

'It doesn't really matter what you say.'

'Never,' she announced tautly, her eyes wide and glittery. 'You must believe every woman that looks at you wants you?'

'Other women aren't important. We're talking about you now.'

She felt madly, wildly, angry and dangerous. 'I should never have come here. I didn't want to. You're shattering kind of people. Why does that woman have to know everything. Can't you leave me even a little bit of pride?'

'Are you going to listen?' he put out his hand and took a grip on her shoulder.

'Not to you.' She tried to push his hand away but he was too strong. 'You won't be satisfied until you own me.'

'Something like that,' he said ironically and it shocked the breath out of her.

'Let me go,' she pronounced tonelessly. 'I can't bear to be here with you, to have to fight you. You've left me nothing. Not even my self-respect.'

'And you've decided Harry and Ellen aren't entitled to their self-respect either?' For a moment his dark face was touched with a desire to hurt her.

'How could they do this to me?' she moaned.

'Oh, stop that,' he said harshly and shook her. 'If you'd stand your ground instead of always running away you'd do yourself a big service. Harry came to me . . .'

'I don't want to hear.'

'You'll hear all right.' He caught the two hands that had come up and pinned them to her side. 'You are the most important thing in the world to them and they were determined you would have every chance. It's not often one sees such love and unselfishness. But then they crashed. You know that. They haven't really picked up since the floods. Making a station pay can be a gigantic task without a lot of knowhow. For Harry it's been a sort of noble dream but he lacks an understanding of what the job is all about. He's a professional man. A barrister. Have you ever heard a more persuasive talker? You must realise

I have a very protective attitude towards Harry
and Ellen. That attitude extends to you, much as
you hate it.'

'Oh, I do!' Because she couldn't move her body
she shook her head from side to side.

'Harry couldn't meet all his commitments, but
what is important, I spoke first.'

'Oh, you never miss the right moment.'

'I wasn't going to stand aside and allow them
both to become frantic with worry. I'm a rich
man, Stephanie. In the fortunate position to be
able to help my friends. I offered Harry a loan
and we talked about it.'

'You talked about me.'

'Of course you. I'd like to slap you for
debasing their sacrifice.'

'As if I'm doing such a thing!' She threw up
her head and tears of fury filled her eyes. 'So you
gave them a loan then you went home and told
the family all about it.'

'Does that sound like me?' he asked furiously
and suddenly crushed her against him. 'You're
the most insulting little bitch I've ever had the
misfortune to know.'

'And you can throw me off Opal any time you
like.'

'I don't need to do that.' His voice sounded
deadly.

'Boyd?' Her head snapped back.

'We're going to find out what's really the
matter with you.'

With her head thrown back she struck at his
chest. 'I hate you for what you are.'

'And what is that? The man you want?' His
arms encircled her so tightly the shape of her
body was impressed on his.

'I have a fiancé, remember?' she cried almost hysterically.

'I don't, because you don't,' he told her oppressively.

'Please, Boyd,' she whispered, suddenly surrendering the fight.

'Please!' His voice was both mocking and savage, 'you perverse little wretch.'

His powerful grip propelled her head forwards and then the darkness dissolved in a shower of light. It was not love. Nor hate. But a nameless mixture of both.

She had never been kissed so violently in her life, and to her shame she wasn't frightened but wildly excited, her head bending to one side while he forced her mouth back taking his superior strength for granted mastering her deliberately until the kiss underwent a startling change; deepening and slowing to a voluptuous mutual exploration as though out of conflict they had come to an understanding. So many years when will had beaten down desire. There had never been a time when she had allowed herself to contemplate what was happening now. Her feelings for Boyd Ballinger she had equated with a kind of madness. She might have her daydreams, feel afraid and even guilty of them, but she certainly never believed that his desire might match her own. The demands that it made upon her might be too terrible to be borne.

'What else are you going to tell me?' Now his hands cupped her breasts and she gasped.

'No, don't.'

'I have to.'

'It's not right. We don't belong together.'

'We're doing pretty well even if you're going to

fight it.' His hand slipped through the draped V of her dress, slipping her bra off her shoulder and finding the naked flesh.

'Please, Boyd,' she begged shakily but his fingers, stirring the rosy peak of her breast, aroused her to such a pinnacle of emotion her body suddenly became subservient to his will.

She arched back her head offering him her ear, the delicate whorls and tender lobe, the long column of her throat, the slope of her shoulder, the satiny curve of her breast. Not only did he take what was so flagrantly offered he held her to him by the hips so the lower half of her body was conjoined with his.

Though she hardly knew it, tears were slipping down Stephanie's cheeks. It was all so terrifyingly easy. She had never believed in such a thing: she and Boyd making passionate love but the question now was not if they could, but if they could stop. Had a bed been available Stephanie was certain she would have been lying on it, victimised by the immense infatuation she had borne silently for so long.

She wished for no more. Life had a way of taking terrible turns. She had lived through a period of great misery and emptiness, now she had the abiding fear love could destroy her.

He was so close to her, so mentally and physically attuned to her he felt her peculiar tension. Not a deliberate withdrawal, more a self-denial. She still allowed him to master her at the same time denying him that part of her that cut closest to her heart.

'What is it?' he demanded abruptly, tilting her face up to him.

'I don't know.' She kept her eyes shut. 'I never wanted this.'

'You've always wanted it.' He cut her short.

'I swear I've never thought of us together. Not for a moment.'

'You mean you weren't prepared for real life? That's what you're not good at, isn't it, Stephanie? Coming face to face with what is real. That's how you got yourself engaged to a man you don't love. The essential missing ingredient. You don't love him. You must realise that.'

A sob broke inside her even as she evaded his question. 'I should never have let you make love to me.'

'I'm sure you couldn't have stopped me.'

'But why, Boyd? In heaven's name, why?'

'You're a dream to make love to. Will that do?' he asked in a very remote, musing tone.

'It's a terrible thing, isn't it, physical attraction?'

'Don't move,' he warned her. 'Can you tell me another man who can bring you so far and so fast?'

This frightened her more than anything else. 'Fifty,' she tried feebly to stay his hand.

He made a funny deep sound in his throat. 'I want to ask you: have you ever allowed a man to take you?'

'The lucky ones,' she heard herself say.

'It doesn't matter.' He trailed his mouth along the lovely line from ear to chin. 'I can find out.'

'Aah.' A spasm of panic caught her high up under the heart. 'The only person who can tell you is me.'

'And you're the only person I'd seek my answer from.'

She was seized by the terrifying conviction

nothing could save her now. 'You're crazy, Boyd,' she panted as he defined her high, tilted breasts.

'We're together in that. I've never met anyone crazier or more complex than you.'

'Don't do that,' she clung to him, her voice a mere whisper.

'Let go, Stephanie,' he urged her.

'I can't.'

He kissed her then with a kind of ravishing gentleness. 'You're crying.'

'It makes sense to.'

He scooped up her tears with the tip of his tongue. 'I have no idea how Anne found out about any of this.'

'Unless you told her.' His tenderness was even more wildly unsettling than the controlled savagery.

'You know I didn't, wouldn't, couldn't. Possibly Ralph let something slip but knowing him I'd say Anne simply put two and two together or went prying into things that don't concern her.'

'She hates me.'

'She seems to.' He stroked her silky, curling mane out of her eyes.

'Why?'

'Maybe she hit on what there is between us.'

'Fear?' Her voice was slightly slurred.

'That's your problem, Stephanie. You're afraid to respond to me. Losing your parents as you did or more particularly when you did made you terrified of risk. You don't want a momentous emotional relationship. You've been through a crucial trauma now you're going to settle for a manageable kind of existence. You're set to tie yourself to a man totally different to yourself.

Your top priority is security. You're like a little girl who finds the thought of love harrowing.'

'Isn't it?' Scarcely knowing what she was doing she kissed him.

'In a way it is. I'm certainly finding it harrowing what you're doing to me now.'

'You started it all.'

'My God, yes.' Beneath his hand he could feel the agitated beat of her heart. 'How long have I known you, Stephanie?'

'Since time began. Nearly ten years.'

'And for the last six of them we've been wrestling with a kind of unspoken, inescapable attraction. You see it as having devastating consequences.'

'I know it,' she breathed. 'Reality is far worse than the imagining.'

'So now you admit it?' He turned her swan's neck so he could kiss it.

'Please, Boyd. Please let me go,' she begged in an urgent whisper.

'All right,' he answered quietly, 'but you mustn't say anything to Harry and Ellen. It would upset them terribly.'

'To think of all the times I've tried to pay them back,' she shook her head. 'They wouldn't accept anything from me but they'd take it from you.'

'It might be because I'm a whole lot better off.'

A night bird began to sing magically somewhere close at hand.

'And is the loan paid off?' she asked as though her heart were breaking to pieces.

'I'm sorry, Stephanie, but I really wanted it all private. Anne hoped to upset us all and she did but don't think for one moment she's going to emerge unscathed.' His face tightened into a sudden, ominous anger. 'I suppose one could find out anything if one set one's mind to it, but Anne took a terrible chance. What happens on Opal, whatever I choose to do, has nothing to do with her.'

CHAPTER FOUR

WHEN they returned to the house, it was to find that Ralph Ballinger and his wife had retired to their section of the west wing, Mark was checking accounts and Cathy was still sitting anxiously waiting for them to return.

'What a tizzy!' She jumped up as soon as she saw them, her skin so milky with distress the golden freckles across her nose stood out in high relief. 'Are you all right, Steph?'

'Of course I'm all right.' Stephanie made a quick gesture with her hand and Cathy flew across the distance between them to grasp it. 'I'm sorry I made such a fool of myself, Cathy. I can see I've upset you. It was so immature.'

'Uncle Ralph was so angry, you wouldn't believe it!' Cathy's eyes found her brother's. 'He wouldn't let Anne get a word out even if she could explain. I've never seen him so totally disgusted.'

'As well he might be!' Boyd's silver eyes were blazing. 'I ought to bar her from the office.'

'She won't be going in there for quite a while,' Cathy said. 'Uncle Ralph was as dumbfounded as the rest of us. I mean he knew about it but he certainly didn't discuss a private matter with Anne. As for Mark and me, it's none of our business anyway. Anne's object was to embarrass you, Steph. In a way she's kind of sick. She's been trying to score points over you for years now. It gets down to jealousy when you'd think she'd have everything she wants.'

78

'Don't worry, Cathy,' Stephanie's head was still whirling. 'I don't intend to stick around to draw her fire.'

'But I want you to!' Cathy cried. 'Damn it all this is my home more than Anne's. You can't punish us for Anne.'

'She's been doing it all along,' Boyd observed dryly, his handsome face faintly hawklike. 'Stephanie would rather reject us all than put a finger on the cause for Anne's taunts. When it comes right down to it Stephanie is quite afraid of involvement. Aren't you, flower-eyes?'

'So I can't handle your aunt?' she challenged him, the effects of their encounter lending a disturbing aspect to her beauty.

'She lashes out at everyone,' Cathy explained. 'She's unhappy.'

'I know that,' Stephanie said very simply still gazing directly into Boyd's eyes. 'She'll make us all ill at ease if I stay. Besides I have Harry and Ellen.'

'And Marcus. Marcus surely?' Boyd asked in hard mockery. 'There has to be some explanation, Stephanie, for why your fiancé drops so completely from mind.'

'I think of him all the time.'

Cathy blinking rapidly looked from one to the other. Tension clung to both of them like an actual garment.

'But surely it would be easier, Steph, if Marcus came here? It's going to be rather a hassle with his leg in a cast. There are so many more people here to look after him and we have the lift that was put in for Grandad to take him upstairs. I just thought we might be able to make him more comfortable and take the extra load off Ellen?'

'I know you mean to be kind, Cathy,' Stephanie said dismally.

'But Stephanie is really thinking of herself,' Boyd declared. 'Can't you see she's desperate to jump up and leave? A strong tendency she developed a long time ago.'

'Please, Boyd, don't be ... awkward,' Cathy begged. 'Can't you stay at least for a day or two, Steph? We won't allow Anne to give you a miserable time. I doubt that she'll even think of it,—Uncle Ralph was so angry. I've never ever seen him come to the full boil. He gave Anne quite a shock. She truly thinks she can get away with anything. Frustrated people do tend to lash out. She should never have married Uncle Ralph and he should never have married her. Both of them seem to have some terrible, unsatisfiable longings and Uncle Ralph seemed to have settled for peace at any price. Until tonight. He really blew up. He even sounded like Daddy used to. The icy rage was so familiar. Mark and I just looked at one another. It was fantastic after all the empty gentleness. Uncle Ralph would have been quite a man if he hadn't had so much tragedy in his life. Certain people can't come back. It was absolutely dreadful what happened to Auntie Margaret and little Phillipa. I don't think I'd survive an experience like that. When I look at my own little son. . . .'

'Cathy.'

'Oh, God,' Cathy groaned.

'Please don't.' Stephanie hugged her. 'If it means so much to you I'll stay for a couple of days. You know I love to be with you but I have Harry and Ellen as well. We so enjoy to be together.'

'Why don't we have them over then,' Boyd suggested rather wearily though he looked the very picture of virility. 'God knows we've got a big enough house and Ernie won't have any difficulty holding the fort.'

'Why that's a marvellous idea!' Cathy's pert face lit up. 'They're both such good company and Harry's stories! Can anyone spin a better yarn than Harry? It would solve everything.'

'If they want to come.'

'They're not like you, darling,' Boyd told her very acidly. 'Harry and Ellen would be the first people to grant me a little favour. And now your dear fiancé is up to his neck in plaster it simply makes good sense. We can call them.'

'Who's we?' Stephanie asked. 'I'll call them. You're far too persuasive, Boyd.'

'Still struggling?'

'What's with you two?' Cathy broke in.

'It's all right, it's been going on a long time,' Boyd declared. 'Now girls, you'll have to excuse me. I have work to do. I've decided to set up a community fund for the few of us who have run into trouble. We're all involved in the same industry so for a while the big will have to carry the small.'

Cathy leapt away to grasp him and pull his face down to her. 'Goodnight, you great handsome hunk!'

'Goodnight, sweetheart.' Boyd's lancing glance shot past his sister to where Stephanie was standing, flushed and brilliant-eyed. 'Don't dream of getting on to Harry before I'm there.'

'No, Mr Ballinger,' Stephanie answered with fierce deference. 'Of course not, Mr Ballinger. Anything you say, Mr Ballinger.'

'That's what you came into the world for, wasn't it, Stephanie, to give me a hard time?'

'Yes.' She was so overwrought she very nearly shouted and though she expected him to turn to the door he retraced his steps very swiftly so abruptly she had to back up.

'Gently, Stephanie,' he warned her reaching out and getting a firm finger-pinching grasp on her delicately determined chin. 'Easy does it with me.' Something very high-mettled and reckless danced in his eyes.

'I'm sorry.' She touched her dry mouth with her tongue.

'That's better.' His eyes fell to her pink, deeply moulded mouth. 'Say good night.'

'Good night, Boyd.'

'You really are very lovely especially when you get flustered. I should think I'd be able to kiss you since I've known you from when you were a sweet little kid.'

She knew she was flushing violently, her violet eyes almost pleading but he just laughed beneath his breath and dropped a brief kiss on her softly cushioned mouth. 'There, that wasn't so bad, was it?'

'Gosh, you're a funny pair!' Cathy exclaimed in a kind of exultant wonder. If only Stephanie and Boyd could care about one another it would be a dream come true.

'We're not a pair at all!' Stephanie cried, flooded by so many contradictory emotions tears stung her eyes. 'I could never summon up the strength to match Boyd.'

'Which brought you to such an extraordinary engagement,' he returned suavely. 'If you're up early enough in the morning, say, six o'clock, we'll go for a ride. At least you've never been in any doubt about my horses.'

'Good idea!' Cathy came behind her friend and put her arm around her waist. 'Let's go upstairs and find you something to wear. I always loved watching you on a horse, Steph. I bet you miss it in the city?'

Though she tossed and turned rather feverishly for much of the night. Stephanie was down at the stables shortly before six. The birds were whistling, calling, warbling in their tens of thousands and she felt her heart lift with the extraordinary beauty of the morning. The air was still cool and so beautifully fresh. She had missed that marvellous, unpolluted purity, the treasury of subtle scents of the bush; all the eucalyptus, their fruits and their flowers, the abundant nectar they produced for the vast legions of birds, the feathery acacias the nations's wattles and the many thousands of species of wildflowers that were still holding in great tracts. Though she was making quite a career for herself in a vastly different world, Stephanie recognised something very basic about herself: she was happiest in the lonely grandeur of the Outback. Even Harry, London born and bred, a once successful barrister, had felt the same compelling love for an Inland of great size. Though he wasn't in any sense as Boyd had remarked a 'cattleman' he was typical of the breed of men who had been drawn to the mighty wilderness. To Harry a close communion with nature was everything and though he had suffered as an inexperienced latecomer, Stephanie knew perfectly well he wouldn't have changed anything. Except the tragedy that had almost destroyed them all. Her

mother and father had come to this country set to
accomplish what Harry had barely touched on,
but that dream, which had seemed so possible
especially as her father and mother had a
background on the land, had been cruelly
shattered. In time Jandra would come to her and
she found herself agonising how she could
possibly live so close to Boyd. Though thousands
of miles often separated neighbours, there were
no closer neighbours than the people of the
Outback. The radio circuit alone would have seen
to that when the great stations and the modest
homesteads came in one by one with their needs
and their news and their problems. Only in
recent times had the vast Kimberley region of
West Australia been granted the marvellous boon
of the telephone through the greatest and
certainly the longest solar-powered microwave
communications system in the world. Across
nearly three thousand miles the towering masts of
the repeater stations rose grey and gleaming
above the blood red earth and the pink and
mauve eroded hills from Port Hedland the iron-
ore port to Kununurra, near vast Lake Argyle
and the great diamond mines; the greatest
breakthrough in communications for one of the
last great frontiers.

'Good day to you, Miss Stephanie!' Wally, the
old stockman called. Once he had been head
musterer on the remotest parts of the Run, now
he potted happily around the stables, grooming
and even singing to his beloved horses.

'The Boss around, Wally?' Stephanie asked.

'He's in there speakin' ta Paddy.'

'Thanks, Wally.' Stephanie gave him a little
wave. 'Isn't it a glorious morning?'

'If it was any better I wouldn't want to die and go to Paradise.'

'You feel sure you'll get there, Wally?' Stephanie laughed.

'I don't see why not,' Wally swept off his wide-brimmed hat and scratched his hairless head. 'I have the comfort of knowin' me muther and sisters have been prayin' for me all me life. No one else would bother.'

Their raised voices had reached Boyd, now he emerged through the archway leading two beautiful horses, his own Bebo with his jet-black coat glittering and a dark chestnut with a regal expression, strong long legs and a wide, fine chest. Duchess.

Smilingly Stephanie walked towards man and horses, stroking the mare's muzzle as she ran a caressing hand over Bebo's satiny neck. 'You've no idea how I've missed being able to go for a ride.'

'Mightn't that be a problem for Marcus?' Boyd asked suavely. 'Is he so much of a stranger that he doesn't know your love for the land, for vast horizons and beautiful horses? It's a big jump to the cut-throat world of business.'

'It's exciting,' Stephanie said, vaulting easily on to the mare's back.

'When you're not filled with nostalgia?' He gave her a sardonic smile before turning to mount Bebo. She had to turn her eyes away from him before they reflected the storm he aroused in her. He looked fantastically handsome even in a denim shirt and tight jeans, the large silver buckle on his belt emphasising his narrowed-down waist and lean hips, his pearl-grey stetson at a rakish tilt on his raven head. His hair was getting a little long and my God she wanted to sink her fingers in those crisp, dark waves. He was too damned good looking, she thought. She had never met a man who could touch him. Never expected to. He was as glittery, as dazzling as some god.

'What the heck are you doing sitting like a stone?'

'Admiring you,' she confessed dryly.

'Then we'd both better do the same thing.' He turned Bebo so the two horses were pressing alongside. 'Are they little mauve shadows under your beautiful eyes?'

'Probably. I had a lot to think about.'

'What do you think will happen to your job if you tell Marcus you can't marry him?'

'You're absolutely sure I'm going to do that?' She tilted her chin and looked down her small, straight nose.

'Maybe you want a little help?'

'Not from you, Boyd.' The thought was so shocking she jerked at the rein and Duchess threw up her head and almost leapt into a gallop.

A white-railed fence confronted them but Stephanie had gone over it numerous times. So had the mare. The Duchess took off and arched into the air and suddenly Stephanie was filled with a wild exhilaration. She could even feel the tiny hairs prickle along her nape. Where in the city could you gallop forever? Where else in the world was there this magnificent primaeval landscape little changed since the Dreamtime? Where else was there a great wilderness of such size? No wonder Boyd was such a marvellous, powerful creature. His life had been shaped by grandeur. Opal stretched beyond the sunrise and that morning she was dizzy with its beauty.

Soon cattle began to press in on them from the left and both riders swerved, heading towards the distant curve of a large billabong. Stephanie had been holding the lead but the mare was no real match for the magnificent black. They pulled away and led through an avenue of trees, birds spinning crazily out of the top branches forming a multicoloured cloud high in the air. Colour even came out of the earth, the crimson of the soil, the blue and the pink, the white and gold and the scarlet of wildflowers the horses hooves spattered as they passed. Every colour of the peacock's tail.

By the time they neared the shining sheet of water Stephanie's blood was running strongly in the unaccustomed exercise. Boyd was still some distance from her and she thought recklessly: 'I'll get even with him!'

He was taking the plain but there was a quicker way to the water across an area littered with exotic palms. She would slow down, she wasn't going to do anything foolish and be pitchforked by the mare. She felt completely confident she could negotiate the rougher patch in safety and reach the lagoon first.

And that was how Boyd saw her when he turned to wave. Girl and horse moving swiftly away from the brightly coloured savannah to the dense belt of bottle and acid greens.

'Blast!' His expression was more graphic than his mild curse. 'Little fool!' She couldn't bear him to beat her in whatever they chose to do. He wheeled the black around then crouching over its neck sent the magnificent animal galloping at full pace. There were all sorts of hazards on that rocky, uneven ground. It looked as beautiful and peaceful as some ancient paradise but snakes often cooled off in the deep waterhole that lay along the oasis fringe.

'Stephanie!' Her name was already on his tongue, his shout ringing resonantly across the broad grasslands.

She seemed to check, then as though oddly elated by the thought of victory rode on.

This time he swore. Violently. When he caught her he wouldn't handle her too gently. She knew enough about the wilderness to exercise more caution.

When a great lizard disturbed suddenly reared up before the mare its reaction was one of absolute terror. It rose on its hind legs pawing the air in front of it while Stephanie fought to stay in the saddle.

'Easy, girl, easy.'

The lizard scuttled wildly away but the mare continued to act up frantically while the brilliant white cockatoos squawked in a hostile flock.

Still Stephanie knew not a vestige of fear nor panic. She had experienced a horse 'going to pieces' on her many times before and she felt she could manage now only the mare finished rearing responding to her tone and made a dash to the water.

They were leaping the naked skeleton of a fallen tree when Stephanie finally became unseated going forward over the mare's ears with a cold, sickening sensation invading her flying body. She had taken a few tosses in her time now she tried to gather her body for the fall.

She thought she heard the roar of the wind as the mare whipped over her then she was hitting the ground and earth and sky blurred together.

Fool that she was. Boyd could only say: 'I told you so!'

For a man who had been used to danger all his life Boyd Ballinger went cold. Now that the Duchess had dumped her rider she stood in the background, the gentlest of creatures only Ballinger wasn't concerned with the valuable mare. He was wholly concentrated on reaching Stephanie and moments later he was swinging out of the saddle the muscles of his face rigid as he looked down on Stephanie's huddled body.

Then he heard her shallow, laboured breath and relief engulfed him such as he had never experienced before.

'Stephanie.' He went down on his knees, turning her very gently.

'Watch——' she said very hoarsely.

His eyes flew over her but at a quick judgment she seemed perfectly all right if one could discount having the breath knocked out of one. In a flash, tremendous relief swerved back to anger.

'I've hurt my elbow,' she moaned to head him off.

'Lie still and shut up.'

'It was your blasted fault.'

He took her arm without speaking, examining her badly grazed elbow. 'My God will you ever learn?'

'Everyone is entitled to take a toss.' She spoke with a lot more bravado than she felt. 'Where's Duchess?'

'Over there.' He jerked his head backwards.

'Is she all right?'

'Well she's standing up which is more than I can say for you.'

'I wanted to beat you,' she announced.

'I know that.'

'The marvel is I didn't only that fool goanna staggered up like a drunk.'

'You can always rely on a few mishaps in this neck of the woods. Even the cows take the long way home.'

'Still it's a magical place.' She was lying back unmovingly on the thick cushion of ground cover, brilliantly patterned with spiky, vivid red wild-flowers.

'What's the matter with you?' he asked urgently.

'Nothing.' She continued to stare up at the peacock blue sky. In truth she was so dazed she was happy not to move.

'You didn't hit your head?'

'No.'

'Let me see.' He encircled her skull with his two hands, his fingertips seeking any contusions.

'You've got a nerve making love to me,' she suddenly said.

'I flatter myself you care more about me than your fiancé.' He looked down at her, her violet eyes and golden skin, the thick deep mahogany of her now tumbled hair. It rayed out around her head and silky strands caught fire in the sun and glowed red. 'Do you?'

'I can only confess to enjoying your kisses.'

'Wouldn't Marcus be offended?'

'I won't tell him.'

'I expect he thought he could trust you to be faithful.'

'And I would have been only you had to make things happen.' She twisted up quickly in an outburst of unfocused emotion.

'Seeing stars?'

'Yes.' She closed her eyes and tipped back her head. 'They're whirling against my eyelids.'

'You shouldn't have swung back into battle. After a toss you have to take your time.'

'I do so try to be calm with you.'

'I do too, but it's no good.' His hands that held her firmly at the waist moved upwards, his long fingers resting against the sides of her high, young breasts.

'You stop that, Boyd,' she whispered.

'In a minute.' He told her rather sombrely. 'You have such a beautiful body. What has your Marcus demanded?'

'As much as I'll allow him.' She put her hand up as he unbuttoned her shirt, her skin golden against the creamy silk, the swell of her breasts blossoming out of the fine, flesh-coloured lace, but her strength, even her will was dissolving against the yearning to have him touch her.

'I've never seen a golden pearl but that's what your skin's like.'

'My head's pounding, Boyd,' she said a little wildly when in reality everything in her was rising to meet him.

'So's mine.' He took a good, deep breath. 'A few minutes ago I wanted to get you the paddling of your life, now the best I can do is shape your breasts. Come to me, Stephanie.'

'For how long?' The urgency in his voice expended the last of her strength.

'For always. From this minute. You belong to me. You always did.'

'No.' She shivered, she couldn't help it. 'No, I don't want to love you, Boyd.' Her violet eyes seemed to turn purple.

'I realise that. I know you very well.' He drew her fully into his arms, moving her body against his, burying his face against the warm fragrance of her hair and skin. 'If you let me I can reach you.'

'Please, Boyd.' She couldn't breathe.

'There's no better way for you.' It seemed impossible but there was a fine tremor in his lean, powerful body.

Before she could protest or say anything his mouth was on hers, his tongue circling the moist interior reaching for the sweetness like a honey eater at nectar.

She was totally lost, his mouth and his strong body pressed against her pushing her beyond the boundaries of the immediate world into an altered state of consciousness. What she did not realise was she was going into a sexual trance, bringing up her arms so they encircled his head, gradually, eagerly, matching his passion so he turned her back on to the grass, allowing his body to sink against hers.

Nothing had ever been like this. No one. There was only one Boyd.

Now his fingers circled her nipples very gently sending little spiralling shocks to the extremities of her limbs. She arched upwards a little in an urgent demand for him to release the catch on her bra. She thought she had never experienced anything so wonderful as the caress of his mouth and hands. He unleashed something in her that was a mixture of exultation and fear. Something that was truly devastating and gaining in power.

She tried not to shake. She wanted to stop shaking.

'Stephanie,' he said above her.

She exhaled a shuddering breath. She had a problem. Maybe she had always known it. She was madly in love with Boyd Ballinger yet she couldn't break out of her self-imposed prison. Rather than put herself in his power she had allowed herself to become engaged to a man who expected nothing more of her than she could handle.

A great sadness overwhelmed her.

'Don't you dare cry,' he said firmly. 'I don't really think I could take it.'

'And I can't take this any longer. Enough, Boyd. I can't even think when you're near me. You seem to deprive me of my own will. It's like a fire that burns out of control. It's all right for you, you're invulnerable, but I don't want to suffer. I've had enough!'

He sighed and lay back beside her, taking her hand and carrying it to his mouth. 'You've never forgotten your terrible unhappiness.'

'No.'

'You feel that loving someone again would be too much to bear?'

'I love Harry and Ellen. Marcus,' she said defensively.

'But no one who makes you forget yourself. But me.'

'You're playing psychiatrist, Boyd.'

'Sure.' His vibrant voice went wry. 'I'm a survivor too, you know, Stephanie, but maybe I've got more guts than you.'

'I'm sure you have.' The thrust brought tears to her eyes. The Ballinger family had suffered their share of tragedies.

'So you're going to kiss the chance of real happiness goodbye?'

'What do you want, Boyd?' she asked.

'You.' His tone wasn't loving, but perfectly hard.

'I mean as what?' she said tightly.

'I'm certain as a lover. Who cares what else?'

'You disgust me.' She swung up.

'It's what you deserve,' he said savagely, 'you shocking little inverted snob. A wife is what I want. I've had my share of women, but when it comes right down to it you're even scared of that.'

'Scared of what?' She tried to pull away from him but he merely tightened his grip.

'Of experiencing the peaks, of being a true woman. You're just some illusion. When I reach out to touch you, you disappear.'

'For survival.' Her violet eyes seemed to be swallowing her face. 'How could I ever suspect you wanted me? I've only been on the fringe of your world really. When I was only seventeen you'd already rejected a dozen dazzling heiresses.'

'All of them still talk to me.'

'Probably all of them are still hoping. I'm simply not grand enough for you and moreover I've got a fiancé though God knows I've forgotten him these last few days. It's very easy with you around.'

'So what do you think, you'd better run away?'

'The barriers between us are too formidable always supposing you're not playing some terrible game. You've thrown plenty of women over before.'

'God help me now I'm stuck with some playboy image. Don't be absurd, Stephanie,' he said cuttingly. 'My hectic love life seems to be some projection of your lurid imagination. I may have been attracted to someone here and there but I've never told a woman I loved her nor have I ever taken advantage of her vulnerability. What affairs I've had were properly chosen and now over. It may come as an extraordinary shock to you but you're the only woman who has ever succeeded in getting under my skin. It could be because you're a raving lunatic.'

'You couldn't be married to a lunatic for the rest of your life.'

'No more harmful than being driven incurably mad by a man like your Marcus. I've never heard another human being complain so loudly. Heaven help him—you—if anything ever goes really wrong with him.'

'It's all right for you, you're Superman,' she said tartly.

'I think it's the very least I can be. I seem to be on call roughly about eighty per cent of the time. More when you're around.'

'You know we clash all the time,' she seized on that fact like armour.

'Why for Pete's sake!' He grasped her shoulders and pushed her down on to the grass again. 'Because there's been nothing else we've been able to do. Do you think I'm so bloody selfish I wouldn't allow you to grow up? I could have taken you at eighteen. You were in love with me then.'

'I never was!' Her skin burned.

'You were so much in love with me at Cathy's twenty-first birthday party I nearly lost my head and swept you off your feet. God, Stephanie, do you think I'm blind? Everything about you has always surged towards me. It's like something you can't do anything about. Something pre-destined. Now like a damned fool you've got yourself involved in all kinds of foolishness. I just don't believe your choice. I suppose if we ever put him on a horse he'd finish in a sanatorium.'

'He can't do everything!' she cried. 'He's very clever in his own way.'

His handsome face went rock hard and the silver eyes narrowed to mere slits. 'If you marry him you're going to spend a lot of your time in bed. Do you want him to do what I'm doing?'

'Don't,' she said faintly.

'Well—so you're still a virgin?'

'Isn't that extraordinary!' she glared up at him. 'Men are beasts, every last one.'

'Demons. That's why women give their hearts to us.'

'You, you're a demon,' she whispered.

He bent and pressed his mouth to a vein over her heart. 'You're what I want.' He seemed immensely sure of himself and strong. 'So I wouldn't advise you to give me any more trouble.'

She closed her eyes moaning slightly and he put his hand underneath the back of her head and lifted her mouth to his.

In the late afternoon of the next day Marcus was released from hospital and flown by a small charter plane to Opal Downs Station. In appearance he was pale and had lost weight and his manner was that of a man suffering a terminal illness with the utmost bitterness.

'Would you like a drink, Marcus?' Stephanie asked when they were alone together in the splendid guest suite that had been allotted to him.

'Bless you,' he said distantly.

'It's a terrible shame this had to happen,' she ventured, trying desperately to feel sympathetic when she was really embarrassed and irritated beyond measure.

'It was no accident, my girl. I think it was your fault.'

'Good grief,' Stephanie shook her head, 'I can't see how you could blame me.'

'For bringing me to this godforsaken spot in the first place. Good God, Stephanie, you know me. How could you possibly think I could fit into the backblocks? There is really no excuse.'

'Backblocks, Opal?' She eyed him as though he were demented. 'You've never been in such a magnificent house in your life.'

'I'm not talking about here.' He took a double whisky from her. 'I'm talking about your people.'

'I wouldn't talk about my people if I were you,' she said loudly, 'it would be dangerous. They made you as welcome and comfortable as possible. Both of them are generally regarded to be extremely good company not the cause for an almighty yawn which I've seen some people do around you.'

'Do you really have to attack me now?' Marcus asked painfully. 'Now when I'm down.'

Stephanie waited and tried to count ten. 'I don't like to say any of this at all but I think it's extremely bad form to criticise one's hosts and when they're my family, wickedly stupid. I know now it was a mistake bringing you out here. Then I thought you might relish the adventure.'

'I avoid adventure,' he said tonelessly. 'Do you think we could stop now, Stephanie? You haven't even kissed me.'

'I don't really fancy kissing you at the moment.'

'Perhaps you find it easier to kiss Ballinger?' he challenged her. 'One can't help discerning a certain heightened atmosphere when he's around.'

'Jealous?' she asked coolly.

'Yes. You're my fiancée. Ballinger certainly can't have you.'

'And why do you want me, Marcus?' She remained standing in front of him, on her face an expression of unhappy puzzlement. 'When we move off our little path of work and dinner and a few parties at your friends we have very little in common.'

'Rubbish! You're talking a lot of nonsense, darling. It's this place, this wild country. It's too big and too lonely. It gives me the creeps. It's obvious you're feeling it too.'

'I love it,' she pointed out quietly.

'Oh, perhaps for a week or so. One would want to be here.' Marcus's mocking glance swept around the magnificent proportions of the bedroom and the sitting room beyond. 'I mean it's so incredibly bizarre. Why would one want a place like this out here? Who's to see it? A palace in the city is all very well—a most comforting status symbol and all that—but here? My God, it's the most incredible indulgence.'

'We all tend to indulge ourselves with our home. You have the best you can buy. This is what the Ballingers can afford. A family like that are very particular about their environment.'

Marcus put his glass down carefully on the small, round table. 'I don't understand you, Stephanie. The little you've told me of the

Ballingers led me to believe you didn't much like them. Especially Ballinger himself.'

'I don't like them,' she said wryly. 'One either loves them or hates them.'

He looked at her very sharply. 'There's something between you two, isn't there?'

'But of course there is! I've known Boyd for nearly ten years.'

'Why isn't he married?'

She shrugged lightly. 'Why ask me? Ask him. Dozens of women have been down on their hands and knees.'

'You, too?'

'Never.' She rearranged a golden rose with infinite care. 'I shall never get down on my hands and knees for any man.'

'I guess that's part of your charm,' he said dryly. 'Darling—listen—I'm sorry. I know I've been a bit of a bore, but I've never felt so useless in my life.' His expression as he gazed down at his plaster encased leg was heart-rending. 'Broken limbs might be everyday occurrences out here but I never thought such a thing could happen to me in my life. I'm absolutely no good with sickness.'

'But you're not sick,' she said simply.

'Well then, I'm laid up. I thought at least I'd get some sympathy from you, Stephanie. You're not at all endearing in your present mood.'

'I'll drop it then. Does that suit you?'

'You've changed, haven't you?' he asked stiffly.

'We both have.'

'Darling!' He propelled the wheelchair that had been found for him right alongside her. 'In that dreadful tunnel, all the hours I was in hospital, all I thought about was you.'

'What did you think?' she turned and looked down at him steadily.

'Why, how much I love you.' His eyes flickered. 'You're so beautiful. Have I ever concealed my pride in you? I consider myself the most fortunate of men. When we're married I'll buy you all the right clothes. You look startling when you're properly dressed.'

'Not now?' she asked in an odd tone.

'In some kind of jillaroo's uniform? You can do a lot better than that, darling. With a few of the little rough edges worn off you'll be perfect.'

'And what's wrong with me now?' she asked slowly.

'Nothing really, darling.' He lifted the back of her hand and kissed it. 'You're so young. Also you tend to be a little sharp-tongued and wilful. Nothing we can't fix.'

'And how am I going to go about fixing you?'

'Darling,' he gave his very regular, very white smile, 'I don't think you can find much to criticise about my behaviour.'

He seemed to be perfectly serious which further confounded her. Why he was nothing more than a selfish, tailor's dummy, which seemed to prove she was a terrible judge of men.

'If you have everything you want,' she said quietly, 'I'll go and see if Harry and Ellen have settled in.'

'Surely they can take care of themselves?' he sulked. 'I can't help thinking, darling, you have no idea what it's like to be in a wheelchair.'

'At least you can give it back in a few weeks,' Stephanie walked to the door and paused, 'try feeling grateful.'

'You were much nicer at home,' Marcus said.

'I guess you were more loveable as well.' She gave him a faintly wry smile. 'The family usually have a drink before dinner. I'll come and collect you about seven.'

'And what am I supposed to wear?' Marcus asked sourly.

'Oh, something smart. Lan Ying will help you. He's looked after the family for years. He was simply wonderful with Boyd's grandfather in his last illness. Please don't complain. He's not used to it.'

'I never do,' said Marcus.

Ellen extended an arm to her when Stephanie walked through the bedroom and out on to the balcony.

'What's the matter, dear?'

'I'm a little afraid of this situation,' Stephanie said.

'Everything will work out. You'll see.' Ellen gave her a quick hug. 'It's Marcus, isn't it?'

'I guess so.' Stephanie stared out over the luxuriant garden. 'I suppose it's just as well.'

'Certainly it is,' Ellen tuned in on the thoughts behind the words. 'I think you've only seen a smooth façade up to date. Now you're seeing Marcus in all his moments.'

'I've made him very cross with me,' Stephanie said.

Ellen gave a nod of rueful agreement. 'You do seem to be out of harmony. I think maybe, dearest girl, you're not really suited.'

'Then why did I become engaged to him, Ellen?'

Ellen was slow to answer, obviously choosing her words. 'I think it had something to do with

avoiding pain. In his own environment I'm sure
Marcus is a very agreeable person. He's good
looking. He can be charming and witty. He's
successful. He owns his own business. He's the
right sort of person to get serious about without
getting really close to. I've always thought all
your strongest feelings were for Boyd no matter
how much you made a pretence of not standing
him. In a way your getting engaged to Marcus
was a rebellion against your long involvement
with this family. Boyd in particular. In some
weird fashion you've transferred all your pain of
bereavement to Boyd. You slipped under his spell
almost at that time.'

'Ellen, dear, this is too complex,' Stephanie
stared at her.

'You are a complex creature, didn't you know
that?' Ellen patted Stephanie's satiny cheek. 'We
all have our little problems. Some are more
severe than others. It's a very great trauma
indeed to lose both parents at the same time. You
were even in a new country. The Outback. A big,
scary world. I know I found the dimensions
awesome even as a grown woman. So different to
what we had been used to. The heat and the sun.
You were an orphan in every sense of the word.
You were also on the brink of womanhood. So
much going against Boyd.'

'But Boyd had never shown the slightest
interest in me.' Stephanie protested.

'No, Stephanie,' Ellen shook her head. 'You
understood he had. At your deepest level.
Whether he said something I don't know but
some little bitterness has been festering there
inside you. I think it coincided with Cathy's
twenty-first gala ball. You had been looking

forward to it with such eagerness, such excitement, Harry and I began planning your own party, then overnight everything seemed to change. You threw up a protective skin that's grown thicker and thicker with time. I think you almost had yourself believing you couldn't stand Boyd.'

'For obvious reasons,' Stephanie said. 'I've always felt strange with him.'

'In terms of what?' Ellen asked calmly. 'You have a great deal in common. Allowing for the flying sparks you both adore the land and all that goes with it. You're both vivid and energetic. You share a great love of horses. When Boyd says something amusing or droll I know you'll be the first one to laugh as he laughs at you. You care about houses, *this* house, heritage, hard work. I know if you married Marcus the life would drain out of you, but if you ever did decide what you really feel for Boyd it will be a positive step forward. At the moment I think you see him as having a threatening image.'

'No doubt a psychiatrist could tell me,' Stephanie gave a shaky little laugh. 'You know, Ellen, you've said more in ten minutes than you've said in years. How come?'

'I'm worried about you, dearest. Harry is too. All we care about is you.'

Stephanie who was taller, kissed the top of Ellen's soft, grey head. 'And I really do love you too. No words can describe how deeply. The both of you are so infinitely caring and unselfish. I know you've had to go without a lot for me.'

'Nonsense!' Ellen wouldn't hear a word of it. 'Is there any greater gift than love? What can you possibly balance against it? Nothing money can

buy. No, you've given us great happiness,
Stephanie. We have every single letter you ever
sent us. All the glowing school reports. It was
like being parents when I couldn't be. You have
Harry's marvellous loyalty, fidelity, the trick of
lighting up the loneliness. Harry still engages me
in the most compelling conversations. Anyone
would think we'd just met. In a sense we're
starved for company, then again no one could be
better company than my own husband. He's
sixty-two yet he acts like an enchanting young
man. I suppose he is a bit demented, turning
away from all he had. It's not as though we're a
great success.'

'What is success?' Stephanie asked reflectively.
'You have just spoken about your husband, your
life's mate in the most loving, affectionate terms.
That's the kind of success most women would
choose. I know you'd be willing to die for each
other. Regardless of money, too much or the lack
of it, you've made a good life.'

'Why thank you, darling,' Ellen rubbed
Stephanie's arm gently. 'I think so too.'

'Do you think Marcus would be willing to die for
me?' Stephanie asked ironically. 'I don't think so.'

'Probably it takes someone very, very special.'
Ellen slotted her fingers through Stephanie's
long-fingered hand. 'Do you remember that time
you went on the branding muster?'

'You mean if Boyd hadn't been around I
probably wouldn't be standing here? Oh, he's
brave.'

'He certainly is,' Ellen smiled. 'Why do you
find it so damned hard to admit you love him?'

'I'm not supposed to love him, that's why!'
Tears sprang into Stephanie's eyes.

'Now what the heck does that mean?' Ellen peered very closely into Stephanie's face. 'It's not every day we happen to get to the root of the problem. What's troubling you, dear? Can't you tell me?'

'I think Anne Ballinger took away so much from me. From Boyd,' Stephanie finally said.

'Anne?' Ellen queried, frowning deeply with her thoughts. '*Anne* Ballinger, of course.'

'That night of Cathy's party, she said the most appalling things to me. I can't even discuss them. I was such a sweet, innocent child. My God, how innocent! Just a young girl in love with love. My thought, my dreams weren't really sexual at all, more delicious daydreams, odd little stirrings. Boyd was, still is for that matter, hero material. One only lifts one's eyes to hero's, not offer them one's body. She spoke to me in a way I'd never known. I think she spoke until she was exhausted. She couldn't seem to help herself anymore than I could unglue my feet from the floor. She seemed to defile my softest, purest thoughts.'

'My dear child!' Ellen's small, work-roughened hand was, as always, tremendously comforting. 'Why ever didn't you tell us?'

'And upset you too? Have you tackle her when you have no stomach for anything ugly. I wouldn't have you hurt, Ellen. Or Harry. It would have upset him dreadfully. And more importantly strained his relationship with Boyd. Harry has a great tenderness for Boyd. Can you imagine that! A big tough guy like Boyd.'

'Tough, maybe. A damned good friend,' Ellen said evenly. 'So all these years you've been taking it out on Boyd for what that woman said?'

'Maybe what she said I would have come to think about. I was certainly madly infatuated.'

'More afraid than infatuated, but never mind. Whatever Anne Ballinger said she said it for no more reason than blind jealousy. Hateful enough as it is, she's obsessive about Boyd. It will destroy her.'

'Why doesn't she go away?' Stephanie said.

'Opal is the biggest thing in Ralph's life. I think he'd die if Boyd told him to go away. The station holds them all together. Its mystique, its demands, and nephew and uncle are really dedicated to one another. That's the sad part. It's a case of a hasty marriage that had no chance of working out. I'm afraid most of the gossip is true. Anne married Ralph to be near Boyd.'

'That's sick,' Stephanie said violently. 'How did Ralph fall for it?'

'I suppose for a time he liked to believe his life wasn't finished. He'd survived a shocking tragedy and Anne in her way is an extremely attractive woman. If she were kinder, more balanced for instance, she would be beautiful, but as it is her expression alone is a pointer to her lack of inner peace. It really is a dreadful, unresolved situation.'

'I don't think I'll ever be able to deal with her,' Stephanie said. 'To me she's poison. She's only happy when she's destroying someone.'

'God help her!' Ellen sighed.

CHAPTER FIVE

To everyone's mixed amusement and malice, Marcus and Anne almost instantly decided they were the same sort of people. It was some kind of miracle. Anne on that first evening came down to dinner prepared to all but ignore Stephanie's upstart fiancé, instead she recognised him at once as someone she could reach out to; someone who knew how to appreciate a beautiful, infinitely patrician woman. Marcus in any case was the ideal dinner companion; a natural facility polished through long practice. He was a very fluent speaker, indeed he loved to talk and like all talkers largely enjoyed the sound of his own voice. He was very good looking in a confident, golden-brownish sort of way. He wasn't at all intimidated by his splendid surroundings and the collection of 'beautiful, batty people' as Harry privately called the Ballingers, and most importantly he knew exactly how to flatter a woman like Anne. In a word, they turned out to be soulmates which, as Harry later remarked 'at least drew Anne's terrible fangs'.

The next day Anne took her place beside Marcus like a woman who had been long deprived of intellectual stimulation and Stephanie, curiously undisturbed by all of this, went out mustering with the men. Soon the Wet would be upon them and every last stray had to be brought in. In the old days it had been a back-breaking job, requiring endless hours in the saddle, now the use of the helicopter and the station motorbikes was proving a real breakthrough.

'Never seen anything funnier in my life!' Harry, who was riding along with Stephanie, was still chortling. 'I had thought you and Marcus were a bit odd together but Marcus and Anne are perfect. Shouldn't be surprised if poor old Ralph doesn't finish in the divorce courts.'

'Do you think he'd mind?' Stephanie remarked dryly.

'Good God I think he's beginning to look on marriage as a bloody curse. Poor old Ralph, how I feel for him! There's nothing spontaneous about him at all, is there? I suppose his spirit and his soul has become numb. Terrible thing that happened to him of course. We who have been blessed can't really see what it's like. Poor old chap can't even conceal his misery sometimes. It shines out of those uncanny Ballinger eyes. I never believed people could have silver eyes, but they've got 'em.'

'Diamonds,' Stephanie agreed.

'They don't seem to communicate at all,' Harry reflected sadly. 'A wise man should never marry a woman young enough to be his daughter. Even then it's lasted longer than we all thought.'

'Yes, hasn't it,' Stephanie observed, her eyes narrowed against the intense glare.

'I know that look,' Harry said. 'I don't think she's as much in love with Boyd as obsessed with him. I mean how can you love a man who appears to abhor you in an entirely civilised sort of way? I think Boyd would like to push her off a cliff only it's not the done thing. She's so spiteful and cruel. I know I'd strangle her. How I thank God

I have my Ellen. We're really the happiest couple I know.'

'I think you are,' Stephanie looked towards him with a gentle, loving smile. 'There's been a lot of gossip going around for a very long time. Do you suppose Ralph has heard any of it?'

'Hard to say,' Harry mused. 'He's not terribly sharp. Listening to gossip isn't part of his life. He's like a man suspended in time. You could say he died with his wife and child. You'd think the Almighty could have spared one of them. I think he must relive their terror. Anyway nothing would undermine his trust in Boyd. You see how they are together. How tender Boyd is to him? Strange fella, Boyd. So many contradictory characteristics flourishing together. An honest-to-God cattle baron which means as tough as old leather, ruthless when it comes to holding Opal together, high-mettled, high-handed, extremely so at times, the last of the kings in their castle, yet kindness itself to anyone who genuinely needs help. I suppose in a way he's a throwback to the feudal system. He's the powerful baron any of his subjects can approach for help. Nothing sinister about Boyd. All out force. Mercifully it's for the good. It's to be hoped he has a son in the same mould. Things might have been rather different on Opal without a man of Boyd's calibre. Mark, for instance, couldn't assume the mantle. The men placate Mark. They look to Boyd for orders. It would still be that way if Boyd were the younger.'

'Yes,' Stephanie agreed, 'only it's hard on Mark.'

'Never mind about Mark,' Harry said blithely. 'He'll have a place of his own when the time comes. He might have been trying to chat you up last night but he's got no show of getting away from the Armstrongs. Old Armstrong wants him for a son-in-law and young Paula is hanging in there for dear life. Only the two girls, you know. Paula and Ruth. Ruth married some Sydney doctor and there's no son. The property has to go to someone. Paula has to marry the right man, someone who can hold on to Merivale as old Armstrong intends. I think it could be the making of Mark and she's a very nice girl. She'll make him happy.'

Stephanie looked at Harry's pink face beneath his wide-brimmed hat. After all these years he still retained his 'English' complexion, and his abundant hair was pure white. 'And you think Anne has been deluding herself in thinking she loves Boyd?'

'I think it's pure theatre. The unhealthy invention of an unhappy, neurotic woman. Do you really think it's love?'

'No, of course not.' Stephanie reined in beneath a red gum and swept her hat off her head. 'Maybe love is only for the blessed few and loneliness for the rest of us.'

'You'll never be lonely,' Harry said. 'You have an enormous capacity for loving.'

'Some don't think so,' Stephanie said a little bleakly.

'Fear can become a habit, darling,' Harry said. 'How can you be a winner if you're terrified of losing? All relationships are a gamble. I can't help wondering about this Marcus. I shouldn't interfere, I know. . . .'

'It's all right, Harry. I value your opinion, you know that.'

'Then he's not for you, dearest. I suppose from inside a relationship one can't see as vividly as the outsider. He doesn't appreciate you. The real you. The mere fact he's drawn to Anne Ballinger should show you that. Then there's another disturbing element. You're not in the least jealous or even a little upset by such interest. In fact you give every appearance of a girl marvellously let off the hook. You can't love him.'

'I don't.' Stephanie pulled at a few leaves and crushing them in her hand enjoying the unique aromatic scent. 'I love Boyd Ballinger and I want it to stop there.'

'Why?'

'You don't seem surprised, Harry?' Was she so transparent? It upset her to think so.

'Now, now,' Harry clucked soothingly, 'don't look troubled. You've covered your tracks very well. Too well if this engagement is a consequence. But Ellen and I are very close to you. I suppose you signalled who you were going to love a long time ago. I know Boyd himself spoke of a "strange tenderness" towards you when you were just a schoolgirl. He enjoyed your company even then. Of course you take after the Sinclairs. Never known to be quiet.'

'He wants a wife,' Stephanie said baldly.

'Who does?' Harry spluttered. 'Did Boyd really say that?'

'He sure did.' Stephanie's violet eyes glowed brilliantly. 'He was very uppity about it.'

'Uppity?' Harry's still beautiful blue eyes looked amazed.

'He's had his share of women.'

'He certainly has.'

'Now he's content to settle for one wife. So he says.'

'Good heavens, surely you're not wondering if he'd be faithful? Ninety per cent of the time he's on the station.'

'Maybe he could arrange to meet them at another time.'

'Them?' Harry questioned giving the word great play.

'I'm just talking nonsense.'

'Maybe a little,' Harry seemed mollified. 'Are you trying to tell me Boyd asked you to marry him?'

'Yes. When I'm engaged to another man.'

Harry apparently didn't find this dreadful for he threw back his head and laughed. 'All's fair in love and war. Why, darling, this is the most marvellous news I've had. Ellen will be thrilled out of her mind. We've always had this golden dream. When you wrote and told us you were getting engaged and you were going to bring your fiancé to meet us, we nearly passed out.'

'So now you tell me?'

'Oh, look, dearest, we were hoping to like him. No, seriously, Good Lord, we were prepared to take him to our hearts. For your sake. But a fella like that . . .' Harry shook his head . . . 'he's not everything a man should be. My dear, I think you'd end up with an awful nagger. How could you ever put up with it if he were ill? Have you ever heard a bigger whiner? It would ruin your life. And the funny thing about people like that, they're surprisingly unsympathetic if anything is wrong with you. Now that you've told me you don't love him, I can tell you I considered him a most unsuitable husband for you. It's your youth and beauty he wants, no more. I suppose you've noticed he doesn't like you expressing strong views?'

He doesn't like arguments, Harry, like you and I. It's our natures to tackle everything from both sides. Marcus finds in-depth discussions useless. He doesn't care for profundities. Actually he doesn't care about much except getting through life as smoothly and painlessly as he can. The terrible things that are happening in the world he prefers to leave alone. It's not natural to him to discuss it. When you got on to capital punishment one night he had the greatest difficulty remaining in the room. Marcus wouldn't care if you hanged the lot of them as long as you leave him alone.'

'Personally I found him a little boring about his marketing policy. And what was the product for God's sake! Some damned soup.'

Everything with Harry was fun. That's why Ellen so loved him. Stephanie had the certain notion all fun with Marcus would stop within three months. She wasn't the first girl to experiment with an engagement and bringing Marcus on to her home ground had saved her all the trouble of making a wretched marriage. She had to tell him without delay but at an appropriate time. With his leg in a cast he was in a sense at a disadvantage. Perhaps she should wait until they were ready to return to the city. She had really liked her job but she knew perfectly well Marcus would no longer consider her.

Ah well! It was not as though she hadn't had another proposal like some shining sword of Damocles hanging over her head. Danger in the midst of ecstasy. If she were to lose Boyd or he were to cast her off, she might be no better than Ralph Ballinger who had been reduced to a shadow of his former self. Some individuals felt more deeply than others and Stephanie knew her feelings for Boyd Ballinger went far beyond sexual desire. So many admirable qualities had been vested in him. In any case, the fault was in her. She was the one who lacked faith and trust. She was the one who continued to act out her traumas.

'I wonder if a psychiatrist could do anything for me?' she asked aloud and Harry looked around at her startled.

'Talking to yourself, are you?'

'I was thinking we could do with a good strong cup of outback tea.'

Harry nodded. 'Well we'd better go and find the boys, hadn't we? You don't know how happy it makes me just riding along with you. Ellen got that excited when Boyd invited us over. Come to think of it, I felt terribly pleased. Opal is very close to Paradise. I've thought for some time someone should write a history of the family and the station.'

'What a good idea,' Stephanie said seriously. 'Why don't you suggest it to Boyd?'

'Well . . .' Harry shrugged a little deprecatingly, 'I was thinking of having a go at it myself.'

'Really?' Stephanie pondered this for a moment, 'Why ever not? You're a great man for telling a story.'

'I think it's important that people know what it was like. I mean this didn't just happen. It's a magnificent story of strong men and women carving out an empire for themselves in a strange land under a searing sun. What drives men and

women like that? Where would this country be
without them? People like the Ballingers carried
British culture, British customs and traditions,
the British way of life to the opposite end of the
earth. The Ballinger family history is part of the
country's history. I think it needs recording, the
triumphs, the deaths and the sacrifices. There's a
wealth of material.'

'Yes, indeed. You'd have all the diaries.'

'Do you think Boyd would be interested?'

Stephanie leaned over and put her right hand
on Harry's shoulder. 'That's like saying do you
think Boyd would be interested in Opal. Of
course he'd be interested. Let's put it to him.'

But Boyd hadn't arrived back at camp.

Harry and Stephanie sat under a tree drinking
their billy tea and munching the freshly baked
scones Bluey, the camp cook, served up and
afterwards came to share with them as soon as he
had fixed the other stockmen up.

Bluey and Harry shared a warm friendship for
all Bluey had had very little formal education and
Harry was amazingly learned. They both loved
the bush with a passion, they were both naturally
good-natured, and in many respects as enthusiastic as schoolboys, though neither of them would
see sixty again.

Bluey was in the middle of a story about one of
the great cattle drives when a young aboriginal
stockman galloped into the camp.

'What is it, Willy?' Bluey bellowed, not so
much angry with the boy for upsetting his story
as irreparably ruining his scones.

'Somethin' wrong with the chopper.'

A half-a-dozen men and Stephanie were sitting
around and they leapt to their feet as one.

'God stone the crows!' Bluey went ashen under his leathery tan. 'Whereabouts, lad?'

Willy was nearly crying, rubbing his hand across his dirty cheeks.

'*Where*, Willy?' Stephanie shrieked. Wasn't this what she was waiting for, tragedy? Dare to think of happiness and the fates would smash it up.

But Willy seemed mad with shock and sorrow, until Bert O'Malley got hold of him with a massive hand and hauled him out of the saddle, holding the boy aloft.

'Orright, we're ready to ride.'

Willy lifted his head and pointed far away. 'Yaleena Pool.'

'Ya sure?'

'Thass right.'

They were saddled in moments while Willy crumpled into a boneless huddle nursing his head in his arms. He had never seen a worse sight than that helicopter quite evidently in trouble. It had just cleared the bulk of Old Garnet and disappeared behind the pyramid-shaped hill.

There was nothing now in the cobalt blue sky. It was empty save for clouds of dust and the ever-circling birds. Stephanie had taken the scarlet bandana from around her neck and tied it over her nose as she rode up front with the lead stockmen, O'Malley and Ranger and Jock McGrath. Harry had fallen right back but Stephanie was riding Duchess—more than a match for the other station-bred horses.

She rode with the speed of terror, her heart in her throat, while other riders galloped in from the direction of Three Mile Camp, all of them aware now the helicopter was in difficulties or had gone down.

As they swung over the hill, O'Malley raised himself up in the saddle and roared: 'God Almighty, look there!'

The blood seemed to drain from Stephanie's head and tiny pinpoints of coloured lights blurred her vision. The helicopter was down there, but half lurched on its side against an outcrop of boulders. Somehow Boyd had set it down in a hazard-filled terrain, but the immediate deadly fear was that the petrol tanks would ignite.

'Let's get down there!' Ranger shouted, bringing them out of their cold, fascinated stupor; then they saw Boyd standing outside the aircraft, then half-circling it at a run, opening out the door and dragging his co-pilot clear.

'*No!*' Stephanie screamed, transfixed by horror. What was her whole life but an extension of tragedy? Now she was to be frozen in terror while Boyd would be engulfed in flames. He was half-carrying, half-dragging the other man and they could tell by the limpness of his head and burly body he was badly injured, or unconscious or both. It was Gibson. They all recognised him now. He was a big, well-muscled man, a dead weight.

O'Malley kicked his horse with his heels. Ranger and McGrath followed him, galloping down the slopes, descending towards the flats at breakneck speed. If those petrol tanks blew! They all knew what that meant.

Stephanie bent her head over trying to pull out of an incipient faint. She was soaked in an ice-cold sweat yet she knew she had to get down that slope. Nothing could stop her from getting to Boyd, though there were worse things than death.

She should have known she would be the one to be left.

When the petrol tanks exploded, two things happened simultaneously. A great ball of fire leapt into the scorching air and a high, piping anguished keening seemed to float across the valley. Harry hearing it drove his horse at a great spurt right alongside Stephanie, grasping her forcibly around the waist at the very moment she blacked out. One of the stockboys was at her other side urging Duchess to be quiet.

Harry didn't even know he was sobbing. 'Stephy, Stephy!' he could see his niece's ashen face and he tried to suck air into his own agonised lungs. The sound she had made had caused his stomach to flip. He didn't think he would ever forget it, the prelude to nightmare.

'It's all right, Mr Sinclair, I'll take her,' came the stockboy's urgent voice. 'There, now, she's coming out of it now. Let me take her now.'

'Thanks, Benny.' Harry's voice was a hoarse whisper. He couldn't bear to look towards the plain or the orange column of flame with blue at its centre. Shock was rendering his old limbs almost useless. Stephanie was lying half-conscious on the grass, the fingers of her outstretched hands giving funny little twitches, and Harry almost pitched forward until he was kneeling in the grass beside her.

'Dear God, *dear* God,' he thought.

The stockboy who was staring down the plain suddenly grabbed Harry's shoulder with such steely force Harry recoiled. 'Hey, Mr Sinclair!' he cried ecstatically.

Harry knew. He just *knew*. He staggered up and stumbled forward just as Benny clamped him violently on the shoulder again.

'It's the *Boss*!'

'Yes,' Harry said, for that was all he could manage.

'Come on,' Benny yelled.

'You go, son,' Harry motioned to where Stephanie was still lying.

'Wouldn't you just know he could step out of that!' Benny yelled, thanksgiving, pride and awe all mixed up together. 'Maybe we don't have to go at all. He's got Ranger's horse.'

'Harry?'

A girl's voice came to them, seemingly from a long way off. It sounded so frail, so damaged, a shiver of fear ran through Harry's wild elation. He stepped back quickly to where his niece lay half curled up on the grass but Benny raced to her, his bony young face glowing with light.

'Get yourself up off the ground, Miss Stephanie!' He fell to his knees beside her, slipping one arm beneath her back. 'They're all right. They're all right. The Boss is riding up the slope.'

'He can't!' Stephanie said, very weakly.

'Easy, son, easy,' Harry warned. 'I don't think she can stand up at all.'

'I guess not.' Stephanie's face and the weakness of her face told Benny the story. 'The Boss is OK Miss,' he told her gently. 'You hear that? He's OK and he got Gibson out. He's as strong as an elephant. Strong enough to pull Gibson clear. It beats the hell out of anything I ever saw!'

But Stephanie had gone into some kind of shock. Her violet eyes slipped blindly to Harry and Harry motioned to the boy to lie her back on the grass again.

'Boyd is coming,' he told her and took her hand. It felt like ice.

'He's dead.'

'Nooo!' Harry shook his head. 'Benny is telling you the truth. Boyd got them both to safety.'

'He's coming now, Miss Stephanie.' Benny raced from his vantage point back to them. 'He can hardly be dead when he's riding up the slope.'

'We'll see,' Stephanie said, very strangely.

A few moments later horse and rider cleared the slope and Boyd dismounted and threw the reins to Benny.

'My dear boy . . .!' Harry's first words came out in an impassioned rush but Boyd didn't appear to see anyone. His left temple was darkly bruised and there were red weals like scratches along his neck and jaw, but otherwise he radiated an indomitable strength.

'Stephanie!' he said and dropped on his knees beside her.

She looked at him, closed her eyes, then rolled her head away from him.

'Nothing can happen to me, Stephanie, you know that.' He got his arm under her strongly and though she lay unresponsive as though she didn't care he turned her so she was half-lying across his body, his arms locked around her. 'Look at me, Stephanie.'

She still had her eyes closed and she gave a peculiar little sob.

'No, I said, look at me.'

It seemed to take her a long time to obey, but at last she raised her darkly blue haunted eyes.

'There is absolutely no way I'm going to leave you,' he said. 'I'm going to live as long as you and longer. I'm going to be around for a very long time.'

'Oh, my poor little girl!' Harry intervened.

'Don't think you're going to give me a miserable time now,' Boyd continued firmly. 'We might have lost the chopper but you haven't lost me.'

'Ahhhh!'

'What did you say?' He dropped his raven head down beside her.

'I think she just agreed,' Harry gave a little, broken laugh. 'Take it easy, my boy. I mean she's had a terrible time.'

'She'll survive it like I've survived it,' Boyd said. 'Isn't that right, Stephanie? I never knew the time you couldn't speak.'

'I——' She put up her hand and he took it and pressed it to his mouth.

'I'm always going to be here, Stephanie, even when the going gets pretty heavy.'

'What did happen, my boy?' Harry gave another one of his wobbly laughs.

'Jack had some kind of seizure,' Boyd explained while Stephanie began moaning softly. 'I'd hate like hell to have to do it again. As it is I think I've broken the poor devil's jaw.'

'My goodness, Boyd!' Harry whispered fiercely. 'Do you mean to say he attacked you?'

'I don't think we could call it an attack,' Boyd shrugged. 'It was more like an epileptic fit yet I'm certain he has never had one before.'

'He's a big feller too,' Benny had crept closer. 'Would it have anything to do with the bad headaches he's been getting?'

'I've just learned about them now,' Boyd returned tersely. 'I wish you fellows would just follow instructions. If there's anyone ill I have to know about it.'

'Sorry, Boss,' Benny muttered. 'He always reckoned it was his eyes.'

'My God!' Boyd murmured with the utmost control. All the time he had been talking he had not taken his eyes off Stephanie's face. Her pupils were so large they were almost swallowing the violet iris and her golden skin had a pallor that bleached it to ivory.

'That must have taken some doing,' Benny looked across at Boyd admiringly, 'fending off Mr Gibson with one hand and landing the chopper with the other. I mean it's the sort of situation you see in a James Bond movie.'

Harry did not laugh. Neither did Boyd.

'Only heroes live to tell the tale,' Benny added.

'It must have been frightful!' Harry reflected. 'It's a great measure of your ability you could land it at all.'

Boyd didn't respond or look up. Stephanie shuddered violently and he enfolded her more strongly, so her head moved back against his shoulder. 'Surely I ought to be the one who's shaking?' he mocked her gently.

'Instead of which you're as cool as a cucumber,' Benny nodded. 'I guess I ought to go and see what's wrong with poor bloody Mr Gibson?'

'It would be a kindness,' Boyd said. 'As to that, he'll have to have some pretty exhaustive tests. If it's all the same someone else can fly him out.'

'Do you think it's serious, Boyd?' Harry asked, after Benny had sped half way down the slope.

'I hope not.'

'Look what he has done to you.' Stephanie

managed her first words, her fingers moving with a butterfly's touch along his throat and jaw.

'The poor devil knew nothing about it,' Boyd told her in a no-fuss voice. 'I'm only sorry I had to be so brutal. Of course he picked the worst possible place for an "incident". Ten minutes before or after and I might have been able to land with no major damage. Maybe just the skid.'

'I expect he'll die of shame,' Harry said. 'My nerves aren't what they used to be. I could do with a stiff drink.'

'We'll go back to the house then,' Boyd said. 'One of the men has gone for Mark. They'll all have seen that column of smoke.'

'They'll be sick with worry,' Stephanie's fingers tightened around his.

'Jock will get to them,' he promised her. 'It's incredible! I had to take up the only man on the station who has had a fit lately.'

'Rotten bad luck,' Harry said.

'Let's write it off as though nothing has happened,' Stephanie's dazed eyes suddenly flashed. 'A bit of bad luck.'

'Don't, Stephanie,' Boyd said.

'I can't stand it,' she wailed.

'I know. I know.' He pressed her closer, lifting her higher in his arms.

'I can't stand the thought of losing you, Boyd.'

'I'm here,' he said harshly, looking down into her agonised face.

Even then he heard the drone of an engine before the rest of them. 'That will be Mark,' he told Harry. 'They'll have to get Gibson back and look after him. Stephanie is all right with me, resting quietly. You'll have to get on to

Gascoigne to Doctor Steele. Fill him in with what's happened.'

'You have to come back with us now,' Harry said.

'Do as I say, Harry.' Boyd didn't raise his voice but Harry stopped insisting.

Mark arrived soon afterwards, hurtling up the hill looking appallingly strained. 'Whatever happened?' he shouted.

Oh, yes, he loves his brother, Harry thought. Beyond anything.

Mark was out of the jeep kneeling by his brother's side, grasping Boyd's shoulder. 'God almighty, I've never had such a fright in my life!'

'I'm convinced I haven't either,' Boyd flashed him a crooked smile. 'Gibson had some kind of seizure. I don't know exactly what it was.'

'What?' Mark cried excitedly.

'He's hardly conscious now,' Boyd said. 'I had to hit him hard before he killed us both.'

'I don't believe this,' Mark muttered savagely. 'There's no more easygoing bloke than Gibson.'

'And I want Doctor Steele to take a look at him just as soon as he's able. Young Benny said something about bad headaches.'

'Who the hell cares about Gibson?' Mark cried. 'He could have killed you!' Mark stopped, breathing hard. 'I just can't understand how you're taking this so calmly. A near bloody tragedy and the waste. Don't tell me. The chopper was blown to bits.'

'I had to bring it straight down with Gibson trying to strangle me and damage the controls.'

Mark sighed deeply with a catch in his breath. 'How can you even talk about it?'

'I'm answering your inquiries,' Boyd said laconically.

Mark stared at him intensely then his eyes travelled to Stephanie who was still lying back quietly in Boyd's arms, making no attempt to get up. 'Is Stephanie all right? She looks strange.'

'Shock, my boy,' Harry told him.

'She saw the whole thing?'

Harry nodded.

'It was a pretty dreadful thing to happen.' Mark crouched over Stephanie and smiled into her eyes. 'Hey there, that was a close shave. Nothing boring on Opal.'

'No.' It wasn't her normal voice.

'We'll stay here for a bit,' Boyd told him. 'Take Harry with you and collect Gibson. He's in a worse mess than any of us.'

'The damned fool!' Mark still reacted hotly. 'Do you want me to come back for you?'

'No.' Boyd looked back at the standing horses. 'Do you feel Stephanie can ride?'

Stephanie's violet eyes flickered. 'I'm all right.'

Boyd's eyes met Harry's. 'A ride in won't hurt her. Believe me.'

'I know.' Harry nodded. 'I trust you, Boyd.'

Mark was standing, looking down at them both. 'Things haven't changed much, have they?' There was a flicker of envy in the Ballinger eyes. 'Seeing you there together recalls a dozen telling occasions in among the camouflage. I'm amazed Stephanie's fiancé doesn't know how little he means to her. A blind man could see the difference.'

Boyd's face tensed for a minute but Stephanie made no comment, neither did she change her expression. She looked curiously like a girl in a waking trance, so unlike her usual self Mark could not repress a frisson of anxiety. Some

pretty brutal things had happened to Stephanie
and God knows she had doted on Boyd since her
schooldays. No other explanation really was
necesssary. The strange repose was a fragile cover
for some pretty high-pressure emotions; emotions
she evidently could not handle.

After the others had gone and all sound, save
the birds, had receded from the valley Boyd drew
Stephanie back into an area of deep shade,
propping himself against the silver, polished
trunk of a tree with Stephanie still lying back
across his arm.

'All right?' His voice sounded quiet and
perfectly normal. They might have been resting
after a long, pleasant ride.

'I think so.' She gave him a small, puzzled
frown. 'I think this is the first time in my life I
haven't been able to get up. Do you suppose
there is something wrong with my legs?'

'Not your legs, Stephanie,' he said fervently.

'You will joke.'

'Who wants to be deadly serious?'

She cast a frightened glance at his bruised
temple. 'I really thought. . . .'

'You can't be rid of me so easily.' His brilliant
eyes looked directly into hers.

'I hate flying,' she suddenly said excitedly.

'No you don't. Flying is a way of life out here.'

'Except for the crashes. There's always a crash.'

'There are a lot more road accidents,' Boyd
said. 'There's Marcus falling over his own feet.'

'My mother and father were killed in a plane
crash.'

'That's right they were,' Boyd looked down
and saw that his knuckles were white. He had
been so busy dragging Gibson to safety he hadn't

seen the helicopter explode but Stephanie had.
Her eyes still had the unseeing look of one who
had witnessed and relived a horror all in one.
'They took off in a clear sky and less than an hour
later flew into a patch of bad weather. It often
happens over our jungle lands. Your father could
have put down on Clavell but he thought he
could handle it. He'd had plenty of flying
experience but under very different conditions.
There's so much to know, Stephanie.'

'Yes, death is ever present,' Stephanie said
sombrely. 'This is a harsh, unpredictable
country.'

'I understand it. You understand it.'

'I understand it too damned well. I don't think
I'd ever know a day in advance if you'd come
home alive.'

'Which would seem to be part of your
neurosis.'

'The fact is you were almost killed today!' In a
devastating reversal she drew herself up swiftly
her blue eyes blazing, her hand clutching and
twisting his shirt almost violently. 'Do you know
how I felt. Do you?'

'So you realised you love me.'

'What did you say?' She blinked fiercely.

'I said, you finally admitted to yourself you
love me.'

'Because I was c-c-crazy with fear?'

'All right then, you hate me?' He challenged
her bluntly.

'I'd be a lot happier if I did.' Her hand was
still clenched around his shirt and as she looked
down almost confusedly she could see that the
force of her pulling had torn a button off. 'Oh,
I'm sorry,' she said in a complete volte-face.

'That's quite all right.' His silver eyes were both serious and mocking. 'Honestly, I have another one.'

'You must be badly jarred, are you?' she looked anxiously into his darkly mocking face.

'No, I don't think so. I've never been one to go to pieces, Stephanie.'

It seemed all too true. 'I always go to pieces,' she told him grimly. 'I wouldn't want to pass that on.'

'True or not, I still want you,' he continued smoothly. 'Did you imagine that little fact was going to put me off?'

'But there is something wrong with me, Boyd,' she sighed deeply and lowered her head, a completely instinctive move that had nothing to do with conscious thought. When she was with him everything was emotion. 'Oh, Boyd!' she moaned softly and pressed her mouth to the hollow at the base of his strong throat, then with slow deliberation moved yearning fingertips gently over his skin. He was so strong and lean and hard. So vital.

'What are you doing, Stephanie?' he demanded a little roughly, his hand suddenly snatching up a handful of curls.

'Loving you,' she laughed a little. 'Isn't that what you want?' She set her mouth against his heart. The things she had seen him step away from. He seemed invulnerable.

'Stephanie, come here.'

She felt the tug on her hair, the taste of his skin in her mouth and she lifted her face blindly at the same time bringing her slender arms up around his neck. She only knew her feeling for him was almost too intense to bear. That she loved him so deeply part of her shrank away from the knowledge in terror. In great love there was great grief, but at that moment she would have accepted grief a hundred times over to be part of him. To be one. To lose herself in him without the terrible tension of hiding part of her feelings away.

'You're a doomed woman, don't you know that?' His voice had slowed and deepened. It had not been his intention to make love to her in her state of distraction but her effect on him was so powerful he too was trapped by desire. Shock had made her especially vulnerable to him but now his own tensions were unleashed, causing him to seize her up so powerfully she gave a strangely savouring little cry.

'I must have you,' he said harshly, easing his hold by the tiniest degree. 'How can you expect me to wait any longer? You who have been inviting me for years.'

He brought her down on the grass, half covering her body with his. He was aware now he was on a dangerous, explosive edge and she would make no attempt to stop him. Could not. Her whole body was straining towards him, wild with longing. She was and had always been so obviously his.

His hand moved alongside her face, his thumb tilting up her chin. Her softly sensuous mouth was already parted for him and he took it with a tender savagery, draining her soul through her lips.

Some little endearment came out on a whisper but he turned his mouth back on hers, crushing it out of existence. A primitive force was growing in him, as powerful and instinctive as a jungle animal and his hand moved to her breast imperiously pushing aside her thin clothing to cup her satiny, sensitive flesh. It was excruciating trying to make love to her when her exquisite body was sheafed in clothes.

And how ill-timed! Here, in the open when anyone could come upon them.

Even then he couldn't stop, moving his mouth to her body so willingly yielded to him. How different it was to his own hard, sleek-muscled frame. How perfectly fashioned for a man's loving. Even her breasts were a pale gold with the nipples like small, exquisite rose carvings peaking against his mouth.

He was holding her so her head was thrown back and she moaned jaggedly, almost drowning in sensation. She too wished to be rid of her clothes, to have his hands and mouth dwell on every part of her. For one man alone she was a sensual, passionate woman an she had spent too much of her time trying to deny him as a lover.

'This is hell!' he suddenly muttered with abrupt harshness, jerking his head away from her.

'D-don't. Don't stop.' Her voice rose on a little trailing moan. How could he cut short such ecstasy?

'You know I have to,' he said grindingly, catching her two hands and holding them together. Two violently opposing elements were at war in him, the drive to take her and the need to protect them from discovery.

'You—you monster!' she gasped, trying unsuccessfully to release her hands.

He laughed shortly, keeping her there, looking down into her startlingly wild and beautiful face. 'There's not a whole lot of privacy.'

'It didn't make any difference before.'

'Let's say you respond too easily to me.' In spite of the mockery in his voice he looked very taut and strained. 'Please, baby, someone might come.'

'Oh, the hell with that!' From passion she was panting with fury. 'Now we've got to live by your iron control. Now he wants her, now he doesn't.'

He kissed her so violently she thought her last breath would be cut off.

'You don't think I want you?' His voice came to her very harshly through her whirling senses and she had to accept it because her wrists were still pinioned.

'So what is it?' she taunted him so overwrought by the sight and sound and scent of him, the symbolic mastery she was actually looking to hurt him. 'Will Anne come?'

The minute she said it she was overcome by shame. Her fury, her feminine ego, burned out in a minute.

He pulled away from her immediately, his silver eyes filled with that terrible, icy light. 'What a fool you are, Stephanie,' he said in a deep, contemptuous voice. 'I wished to spare us both embarrassment. Or wouldn't it embarrass you to be found naked in my arms?'

'I'm sorry.' She lay back with her shaky fingers at her temples. 'That was unforgivable.'

'When has the unforgivable bothered you?' His long shadow fell across her.

'So you've always known I go to extremes. I love you and believe me, I hate you too.'

'I can deal with your so-called hate!' His steely anger was a tangible thing. 'Get up and don't let's waste any more time.'

'Actually,' she muttered tightly, 'I want to be alone.'

Without even exerting himself he reached down and hauled her to her feet. 'And you will be if you don't grow up.'

He had the bruised side of his face turned towards her and she almost burst into tears.

'As it happens,' he told her bitingly, 'you're a little sadist. You offered me your body today which is perfect by your timing, but if I came to you tonight you'd be screaming bloody murder. As it is I think it's going to finish up rape.'

'Please—please, I'm sorry.' She stood on tiptoe and tried to kiss his chin.

'Stop that,' he said violently. 'I've had enough.'

'Ohh!' Her breath was coming very shortly and now the tears did splash on to her face.

'Stephanie!' Now at last he looked at her, half-expecting a spitting kitten instead of which her violet eyes were melting jewels. 'I didn't want you to cry.' He caught her to him and she clung like a helpless child. 'Flower-eyes?'

'I . . . didn't . . . mean . . . what I said.'

'You must be the only one who doesn't love to gossip.'

'You must know she wants you.' She dropped her head against his shoulder.

He swore violently and without apology, clutching her even harder. 'Then wouldn't it be a good idea if we moved fast? You can hand Marcus back his ring. Incidently I don't care for his taste, and I'll explain that you've really loved me all along. I don't think he'll dare to fight me with a broken leg. He may even take some of Anne's unbridled passion off me. I have never had the slightest interest in her. You understand that?'

'Of course I do!' she said passionately, trying to coax him out of his intimidating mood.

'Then prove it, you little witch,' he said curtly. 'Opal needs a mistress. I need a wife. No, it's useless to try and twist away. It will all end up the same way. I'm sorry, but you have to marry me. I refuse to be seduced if you're only going to see me in between fiancés.'

'I need time, Boyd,' she gave a little despairing cry. 'If I didn't care about you so much!'

'Boy, are you crazy!' He gave her a pitying, narrow-eyed look. 'You can come close to marrying a man you certainly don't love, yet you live in terror of a man you do love. At least you're not dull.'

'One night I might let you make love to me,' she said.

'Not tonight?' He laughed briefly. 'Tomorrow night?'

'You were sure of me today.' She lifted a flushed, confused face.

'And I'll be sure of you again,' he told her derisively—almost. 'You seem to be one of those women who might well have to be overpowered. I've managed to keep my hands off you for years but now I'm throwing all my fine principles to the winds. You're confronted now, Stephanie, by a man who means to have you. There's nowhere you can run. Nowhere you'll get lost. You're going to be my wife and my problem. Got it?'

She didn't answer, but she didn't shake her head and as they turned to go after the horses they could see in the distance two of the station's vehicles travelling at speed towards them.

'Do you want to apologise for ridiculing my lack of daring?' he drawled.

'I certainly do.' She was appalled now by her own abandonment. 'People shouldn't love each other where they can't rely on being alone for five minutes.'

'Or one of them takes on a fiancé for extras.'

'That's my affair,' she said foolishly.

'All the more reason then for you to work it out for yourself.'

CHAPTER SIX

AT her first sight of Boyd, Anne literally hurled herself at him, crying his name. The agonising went on for a full minute or so while the rest of them stood about trying not to focus on this unbelievable scene. Even Harry had little to comment though he and Ellen flanked Stephanie closely, at least close enough for one of Harry's usual asides, but all of them were held startlingly in thrall by this most convincing proof that Anne Ballinger's affections for her husband's nephew weren't at all 'aunty'. The mercy was that she was quite incoherent.

At last in a somewhat awkward, embarrassed fashion, her husband dragged her off giving the impression that in a morning of almost total chaos and destruction this was the most ghastly thing of all. In any event Anne pushed away and went to stand by herself at the jeep sobbing like a woman half out of her mind.

Capable and kind-hearted Ellen went to her and was waved away violently but Ellen who had considerable authority persevered where a less warm-hearted person might have chosen to make a counter suggestion. She gave Anne several encouraging little pats, put her arm around her and directed her into the jeep then with an all-encompassing wave to the others climbed behind the wheel and rightly or wrongly sped away.

'Trust Ellen to accomplish what the rest of us

can't!' Harry muttered admiringly. 'I don't think I've ever seen such *angst* in my life.'

'My God!' Stephanie was shaking. For so long everyone had kept their private thoughts to themselves; now what no one wanted to face was out in the open. So many people hung-up on Boyd! Ralph was now speaking to him with great kindness and anxiety proving it would take far more than an erring wife to upset his attitude towards his favourite nephew but then the Ballingers, Stephanie thought wryly, set great store by family. Nevertheless it was high time Ralph Ballinger put his house in order and there were certain things Stephanie had to do herself.

In the afternoon the Flying Doctor Service flew in and the unfortunate Gibson who was still in a dazed state taken away, as soon as it was established he had indeed suffered a full-blown seizure the causes for which required neurological tests. Even in his reduced state he had tried to say how sorry he was—he could scarcely account for his sudden violent attack—but Boyd had taken a remarkably philosophic view of the whole situation. It simply didn't occur to him to blame Gibson. The real worry was, what was wrong with the man? Gibson had been in Ballinger employ for close on thirty years and station loyalty worked two ways. The topic of the day was not so much the destruction of valuable aircraft and a double tragedy averted, but rather the pessimistic assumptions Gibson had a brain tumour. A diagnosis that very bleakly turned out to be true.

'I'm blessed if I know what to make of this place at all!' Marcus told Stephanie, at the same time shaking his head. 'Ballinger's self-assurance is devastating. He seems to have a contempt for everything, including death.'

'I think he was a bit shaken in his own quiet way,' Stephanie said. 'He's not given to making a great fuss.'

'And all the talk about the stockman! I mean who the hell would care about a stockman. He's nothing!'

'He's worked here on Opal for thirty years. That explains it. How do you think Boyd commands such loyalty from his men?'

'I expect they're well paid,' Marcus gave a frosty smile.

'And they're well looked after. There's no one on the station who can't depend on Boyd for help.'

'They ought to call him My Lord,' Marcus said sneeringly. 'He wouldn't be one half so damned lordly without all this.'

'The self-confidence is quite natural,' Stephanie pointed out.

'Even *you*,' Marcus looked across at her sharply, 'pay homage.'

'And what does that mean?'

'I can't tell you how I feel!' Marcus hissed. 'I'm a different man out here. It's not my world. It makes me helpless.'

'That's your leg, Marcus.' Stephanie reached out and touched him with her hand. 'I'm sorry it happened. It has spoilt your holiday.'

'And what's wrong with Anne? She's been in her room all day and she didn't come down to dinner.'

'You like Anne don't you?' Stephanie asked, albeit in puzzlement.

'Of course I do,' Marcus slid back wearily in

his armchair making minute adjustments to the placement of his injured leg. 'She's a very attractive and charming woman.'

'She's attractive, certainly.'

'You simply don't approach her, my dear, in the right way.'

'She has always shown me excessive hostility,' Stephanie said.

'Perhaps she doesn't care for your rather high-spirited ways,' Marcus suggested blandly. 'I know you'll learn a little more poise but at the moment you have an excess of youthful vitality.'

'You seemed to find it wonderful before,' Stephanie remarked wryly, looking down at her bare hands.

'I do find it wonderful, darling,' Marcus exclaimed, 'but in judicious quantities.'

'Anything else?' Stephanie raised her dark brows.

'Yes,' Marcus frowned. 'I've been meaning to ask you why you're not wearing your ring.'

'I had taken it off for safety,' Stephanie said, 'but maybe it's better if I leave it off altogether.'

'Now, now,' Marcus clasped her wrist very tightly, 'I don't want any more drama. Haven't we all had quite enough for one day?'

'Actually you missed it,' Stephanie said.

'Thank God!' Marcus said feelingly. 'A remarkable guy, Ballinger. Of course he's had the extraordinary advantage of being brought up in the wilds. Dodging death is not the way I'd choose.'

Something in his precise words made Stephanie slump forward in her chair. Reaction, she thought. I don't want to know it. How many times had she seen Boyd dodge danger? But nothing like today.

Marcus stared at her, his face tight. 'It's a good thing we're engaged, Stephanie, or I might misunderstand.'

'Misunderstand what?' She threw that sumptuous dark mahogany hair back and glanced at him with troubled, violet eyes.

'Ballinger has a hold on you even if you don't particularly like him. Or is that just a front to hide your true feelings?'

'What would you say if I said I loved him?' Stephanie asked simply.

'My dear girl, you couldn't take it. Not at all. You have a lot of anxieties swimming around your little brain.'

'Which is nevertheless equal to yours, thank you very much.'

'I didn't mean it that way,' Marcus said irritably, 'you overdo the feminist bit, if you must know.'

'I suppose it comes from being talked down to daily,' Stephanie stood up and walked to the window. 'I'm quite valuable to the agency, Marcus. I come up with quite a few good ideas for which you inevitably take the credit then smooth me over by taking me out to dinner. You don't pay me as much as Bob and Howard though we all know I can match them and often do better and I'm expected to work in the smallest and noisiest office. That goes without saying. Bob and Howie might complain. Not Stephanie. She never complains. She can't expect to have the same standing as the men. Neither can your secretary Heather without whom you'd be lost. Heather is a real power yet she gets small change as well.'

'I never realised you were upset about money,' Marcus said. 'Ever since you joined me you've never stopped moving up.'

'I should think so,' Stephanie said dryly. 'I've won the agency a few valuable accounts.'

'And I'm very proud of you.' Colour touched Marcus's cheekbones. 'If you want more money, no problem.'

'I don't think I should have to ask, Marcus. The men expect it when they come up with something terrific, but I could wait forever.'

'My dear Stephanie,' Marcus said aggrievedly, 'no one could say I haven't given you the opportunity to shine. You're the most pampered member of my staff.'

'Rubbish. You mean you give me flowers when I work until ten o'clock at night. I'm grateful for your encouragement but I'm quite certain you would have sacked me if I couldn't come up with the goods. You like me to look so smart and fashionable all the time and to be quite frank it's a little difficult to manage. You should be paying me at least as much as Bob.'

'You've got years yet,' Marcus just looked at her.

'No, I haven't. Aren't we supposed to be getting married? Don't you want to raise a family?'

'Not particularly,' Marcus said rather nervously. 'I daresay I wouldn't object to one. I suppose a man should have a son but surely there's no hurry? What we're doing is exciting. Ours is becoming one of the biggest and best agencies in town. And you, my love, are fantastic. The clients love you. Especially the men. You can even make that old bitch Magda Stellmach like

you. We're going to make a marvellous team. You
can't be too impatient, my darling. You're young
yet. When we're married I'll make you a suitable
dress allowance. Your looks, the way you dress,
your style, all these things are important. Old
Man Morrison adores you.'

'You mean he knows I work hard and I'm
smart.'

'Well you're not quite ready to take over my
job,' Marcus said smugly.

'Not to mention the star role as your wife.'
Stephanie took a deep breath and turned around.
'I'm very sorry, Marcus, but I realise now I can't
marry you.'

'Oh, knock it off, darling,' Marcus said sharply,
'it's what you've wanted since we met.'

'I never even thought of it,' she said. 'I would
never have thought of it only you started chasing
me around the office for God's sake.'

'You needed a little persuasion to make up
your mind.'

'Probably,' Stephanie agreed wryly. 'I suppose
at the office we shared the same interests, but
away from it all the problems arise.'

'What problems?' Marcus asked scornfully. 'I
think that uncle of yours has been trying to turn
you against me.'

'No one could turn me against you if I loved
you,' Stephanie said quietly. 'I'm very sorry,
Marcus, I don't want to hurt you. . . .'

'Well you're doing it pretty well!' Marcus
suddenly exclaimed in a cold fury. 'Why don't
you sit down beside me and calm down. Things
haven't been going well for us from the moment
we came out here. Neither of us has been able to
relax and now I'm in a bloody wheelchair. I think

I'd kill you, Stephanie, before I let you get away
You're what I want. You're beautiful and you've
got lots of talent. You'll be even better when you
get older. You don't think I'm going to let
someone like Ballinger or your Uncle Harry drive
a wedge between us? It's taken me a long time to
find someone like you. I knew the moment I set
eyes on you I was going to ask you to marry me.
I've never had any trouble making the really big
decisions. I even knew though you look as sexy as
all hell you'd been a good little girl. You've never
slept with a man, have you? Why do you think
I've been so correct? Because, little Stephanie,
I'm going to teach you all there is to know. It's
going to be beautiful and I think it's about time
we set a date.'

'I don't love you, Marcus,' Stephanie said
miserably.

'Try walking out on me and I'll murder you,'
he said.

'That won't be easy from a wheelchair,'
Stephanie returned tartly. 'Don't threaten me,
Marcus. When are you men going to learn?'

'And when are you going to know your own
mind? Only a month or so ago you agreed to
marry me. You accepted my ring. Now all the
excitement and the romance has worn off. If you
don't love me you should never have said you
did,' he cried bitterly.

'I don't actually think I said I did,' Stephanie
pondered. 'I don't think we discussed love at all
but looking after the business.' She slipped back
into an armchair, her long curling hair brushing
against her neck and cheeks. She was wearing a
short dress in a beautiful shade of pink, the full
skirt barely covering her knees, the tank top

dipping low enough as she bent to show the shadowy cleft between her high, young breasts. 'I don't want to hurt you, Marcus, but as I've discovered now I don't love you, what would you suggest?'

'I'd suggest you come back with me to where you belong. We have no problem at home. Our tensions are created by being in this place. By outside influences. Deny it all you like, but I know your uncle is working against me. He didn't take to me from the moment I arrived.'

'I can assure you Uncle Harry wouldn't interfere in my decisions.'

'Like hell he wouldn't!' Marcus fought back. 'After all they both worship Ballinger, don't they? No wonder he's the way he is when he's accustomed to so much adulation. It can't do him good.'

'You mistake respect and admiration for a lot of soft soap. You don't understand, Boyd, Marcus. You don't know what he means out here. He's a rock. He's the man a lot of people go to when they're in trouble. I'll admit a lot of people talk taffy around him, but after all that happens a lot with rich and powerful men. Boyd knows how to separate sincerity from sycophancy.'

'And why isn't he married?' Marcus asked with barely controlled jealousy. 'Who the hell is going to inherit all this?' Marcus let his eyes flash around the sitting room with its comfortably ambience of space, antique furnishings from a vast collection and arrangement of books and paintings. 'I'd be scared of owning all this. There have to be problems associated with owning and maintaining houses of this size. They're not practicable. Just some grand spectacle. Any heir to this might find it a burden.'

'Never!' Stephanie's eyes flashed. 'Boyd's son will feel exactly as he does.'

'Well it's none of our business, is it?' Marcus looked at her with flickering, narrowed eyes. 'Why are you getting so heated, Stephanie? Your eyes are flashing and your cheeks are flushed.'

'I don't like to hear you attacking your host.'

'You're becoming quite silly, darling,' Marcus laughed. 'I'm merely making a few observations. You're the one who's getting carried away.'

He looked tired, Stephanie thought and his tight smile was a grimace. She stood up and touched him on the shoulder. 'Is there anything I could get you?'

'It's good of you to sit with me at all.'

She lent down in compunction and kissed him on the cheek. 'I know it's no fun for you being laid up.'

'We have to get home, Stephanie,' he said, catching her wrist very strongly so instead of standing she was rather forced to kneel. 'Ballinger is a great man for making arrangements and he has plenty of money to boot. I really think we should get out of here as soon as possible. Hopefully as soon as he can arrange it. I don't trust these modern-day princes. And I can't afford to allow you any more time under his roof. It's hard to say exactly what it is between you, but I can't think it's good for you. Why you could be in moral danger.'

'What?' Stephanie stared at him with huge eyes.

'Seduction—you know what that is?'

'I've heard of it.'

'Or have you already been in Ballinger's bed?'

Stephanie went to pull away violently, but he propelled her forward, his arm like steel across her back.

'Kiss me.'

'I don't want to,' she said furiously.

'I wonder why?' Marcus asked growlingly, digging his fingers into her waist. 'You are my fiancée and I want you.'

'Let me go, Marcus, you're hurting,' Stephanie protested. 'Oh, do let's stop this.'

'I always thought I could trust you, Stephanie,' he said. 'But a man can never tell. You might be trying to sink your nails in me but I'll bet Ballinger has found you surprisingly submissive.'

'Please, Marcus,' Stephanie could not suppress a faint little sob. After all he was her fiancé. She had given him to understand she would marry him. He was to a certain extent incapacitated although he was holding her man-fashion in a brutal grip and she was hurting him with her strange resistance. He had a right to be jealous.

'Darling!'

The general direction of her thoughts had caused her body to untense and Marcus took this as an obvious sign she was beginning to share his heady excitement. Rather gloatingly he caught her mouth, his breath with the tang of whiskey at the same time thrusting his hand into the low neck of her dress very intimately. 'Darling!'

It was the first chance Stephanie had. She pulled back and tossed her head, torn between wanting to dash his strangely repellent kiss away with her hand and not wanting to offer him insult.

'What's the matter now?' Marcus asked dazedly.

'I thought I heard someone at the door.'

'My God, but you're an awful——'

'Hush!' Incredibly there was someone at the door.

'Marcus?' They heard someone call.

'It's Anne,' Marcus whispered harshly.

'The night grows wilder!' Stephanie jeered. 'Ask her in.'

'I can scarcely keep her out. Come,' Marcus called, fighting for his composure.

'I'll leave you two together,' Stephanie joked.

'Oh, damn you, Stephanie!' Marcus was almost beside himself, for the first time in his life without the use of his legs. He seemed to be circling unconsciously in his chair rather like a floundering fish Stephanie thought fancifully and on a wave of sympathy caught his shoulder and began massaging it gently.

Immediately Marcus thought Stephanie had given in and covered her hand gratefully with his.

'I'm not . . . oh, I'm sorry . . . I didn't. . . .'

'Please come in, Anne,' Marcus called charmingly. 'How nice of you to visit me. I was just saying to Stephanie how much I missed you at dinner.'

Anne seemed to be moving towards them in a trance. She was dressed in a very beautiful and expensive housegown in a delicate shade of aquamarine and her blonde hair swirled around a face that was still very white and strained. Almost in a matter of hours she had aged five years.

'How are you now, Anne?' Stephanie heard herself asking.

'I'm fine, thank you.' Anne looked at her from

a great distance. 'I wonder if you'd mind if I spoke to Marcus alone?'

'Why of course not!' Stephanie said politely, glancing long enough at Marcus to catch the mingled gratification and anxiety: this might be a cry for help. Socialising with Anne was one thing; helping her with her troubles quite another.

'Goodnight, dear.' Stephanie bent over and kissed Marcus's cheek not knowing she sounded anything but loverlike.

'I'll see you again tonight, won't I?' Marcus was determined to allow himself an escape hatch.

'I'll look in for a minute.' Her fingers smoothed the fair hair from his temple.

'Ridiculous,' Anne said. 'Such a charade!'

'I'm sorry?' Marcus looked at Anne questioningly.

'I think you should know the truth here and now.'

'I think you should mind your own business, Mrs Ballinger,' Stephanie said sharply, feeling her hot temper rise.

'What we're talking about is my business,' Anne said.

'I'm not enjoying this very much,' Marcus said shortly. 'What is it you want to see me about, Anne?'

Anne turned to face him in her long, floating gown. 'You don't know about your fiancée, do you?'

'Do you?' Marcus challenged her. 'I know you dislike Stephanie for whatever reason. Actually you're one of the few people who do.'

'You can accept that she's in love with another man?' Anne asked very clearly.

'I beg your pardon?' Marcus's attractive voice trembled.

'You . . . just had no idea, did you? How I feel for you. She's lied to you and betrayed you.'

'No, no . . . don't say that.'

'What an extraordinary woman you are, Mrs Ballinger,' Stephanie said almost quietly, 'and how much you hate me.'

'Please, I hope this isn't going to be one of those scenes?' Marcus cried in horror. 'It all seems so terribly unfair when anyone can see I'm almost totally helpless to do anything about it.'

'What is it you do want to see Marcus about?' Stephanie asked aggressively, thinking there was no help at all in allowing Anne the whip hand.

'I think that has nothing to do with you,' Anne went on in that strangely empty tone.

'I must remind you, Anne, that Stephanie is my fiancée,' Marcus said very sternly, his fastidious face expressing his distaste for all female confrontations.

'However you managed that, I don't know,' Anne laughed oddly. 'She's been in love with Boyd incredibly from the age of fourteen.'

'Yes, she's had some kind of fixation on him, I gather,' Marcus said crossly. 'I'm not a fool you know, Anne. I can see some kind of obsession. Damned unhealthy if you ask me. But I can handle it. The infuriating thing is I'm down at the moment. Absolutely felled. I've never had anything like this happen to me before.'

'Then it doesn't matter a great deal to you that your fiancée doesn't love you?' Anne understandably was rather confused.

'Of course she loves me,' Marcus said. 'She's young you know. Twenty-three. Fantasy. All this is fantasy!' Marcus waved his hand. 'Stephanie has tons of imagination. She likes plenty of drama. Ballinger is a mad infatuation. That's about the sum of it. There's no threat from him. It's clear he'll be wanting a different sort of woman. A woman, if I might say so, rather like yourself.'

Anne stared at him as though he showed great perception. 'Yes,' she said faintly.

'Oh for God's sake don't give this lunatic woman any little morsels to feed on,' Stephanie burst out.

'What did you say, darling?' Marcus asked.

Stephanie despised gossip so she kept quiet, muttering little exclamations of protest.

'You realise,' Anne said vaguely, 'that Boyd might have married me?'

'Bunkum!' Stephanie cried ringingly.

'I wouldn't be surprised if it weren't true,' Marcus looked up at Stephanie in mixed warning and censure. 'I say, Anne, won't you sit down?'

'Of course he loves me, but so many things stand between us.' Anne drifted Ophelia-like into an armchair.

'I'll say!' Stephanie snorted. 'There's your husband for one, though you've shown him so little love and attention he'd show few ill effects if you departed. That's one. Two, you must be mad if you think Boyd is, was or ever will be interested in you.'

'Oh, he wants me,' Anne said.

'My dear Anne!' Marcus looked up at Stephanie. Get me out of this, his face said.

'There's a great deal you don't know, Marcus,' Anne said. 'Family relationships are very complex things.'

'Especially to the demented,' Stephanie said tartly. 'Why are you saying all these things to Marcus? It shows what you know about Marcus. He hates anyone to unload their troubles on him. I really think you should go back to your husband. Try to talk this whole thing out. It has nothing to do with Marcus and me.'

'I nearly lost Boyd today,' Anne said.

'You see, that's the trouble,' Marcus said, 'she's in shock.'

'I think she is,' Stephanie said pityingly. 'The thing is how to get her back to her part of the house.' As far as she knew Anne had been sedated.

'I felt I could talk to you, Marcus, the moment I met you,' Anne said.

'My dear you can. Believe it.'

'I married Ralph to hurt Boyd.'

Oh, yuck!' Stephanie burst out in disgust. 'Poor old Ralph didn't deserve that. Don't you know how much he's been hurt. Oh, how cruel!'

'Please, Stephanie,' Marcus protested. 'Go on, Anne.'

'It was a bizarre thing to do but Boyd and I had quarrelled violently.'

'You were ... friends?' Marcus inquired tactfully.

'We were lovers.'

'Rubbish!' Stephanie said heartily. 'This poor woman has blown her mind.'

'No one likes to hear the truth,' Anne answered very quietly. 'Boyd has been my lover before and after my marriage.'

'Oh, really!' Marcus said in a clipped, disgusted tone while Stephanie almost fell on her knees.

'Oh, you liar! You colossal liar!'

'Just ask him,' Anne said.

'I wouldn't even talk about it, it's so dishonourable,' Stephanie said. '*You're* so dishonourable.'

'Like you, I suppose,' Anne retaliated, 'I'm just sorry for Marcus.'

'Thanks,' Marcus laughed sharply. 'All right, Anne,' he said, 'you want to get something off your chest. I think I can tell by looking at her what goes on in a woman's mind. You came here to make me aware there's something between Ballinger and Stephanie. I know that and it doesn't bother me. At least it won't bother me when we get home. This Outback is decidedly hostile to me and now that I think about it, it can't be good for you.'

'Of course it's not good for me!' Anne cried.

'Then surely you can persuade your husband you need more life? I understand that he's a rich man. Besides, there's this business with Ballinger. If he did care for you, my dear, from what I've seen he's long since ceased to.'

'What?' Anne turned on him, astounded.

'Do face the facts, my dear,' Marcus urged her. 'This is mad what you're saying. Monstrous, really. I can't understand how your husband is taking it so quietly.'

'Because he'd die if he left Opal,' Anne cried. 'This is his home. It's all he's got left to love.'

'You don't feel he needs you?' Marcus asked.

'Oh, he's too old for me,' Anne said. 'He's actually too old to go on living.'

'But he's a man in his prime!' Marcus protested. He dreaded growing older himself but calling a man in his early fifties 'old' was too much.

'I think what Anne means,' Stephanie said gravely, 'is Ralph hasn't been a whole man since the tragedy.'

'But he's got Anne, hasn't he?' Marcus countered impatiently.

'It would finish a lot of people, Marcus,' Stephanie said heavily, feeling Ralph's great grief. 'We're all different, you know. My heart aches for him when I think of his mortal pain. And hasn't Anne offered him further injury?'

Anne flung her blonde head up, white lines of rage running from her nose to her mouth. 'I'd rather you didn't give us the benefit of your assessments.'

'People who lash out at others generally take that view,' Stephanie pointed out. 'You told us yourself you married Ralph in the mistaken belief you would hurt Boyd. Ralph would have found out very quickly you didn't love him. I think he'd been made so desperately unhappy your betrayal didn't assume the proportions it might have if he hadn't had such a hell of a life. Why don't you ask him for your freedom?'

'You're extraordinary!' Anne gave a wild laugh.

'We've only one life. Do you want to live it in utter misery?'

'I promise you that you will if you try to get Boyd,' Anne said with deadly softness. 'I can't let you have Boyd. Oh God, no.'

'Why not?' Stephanie asked austerely. 'Someone has to get him, Anne. He will marry and soon.'

'I won't mind so much if it's not you,' Anne continued in that low, venomous tone. 'I really don't know why I hate you so much, but I do.

I've hated you since you came here as a simpering little schoolgirl looking at Boyd with your big eyes.'

'Simpering? That's good,' Stephanie's young voice was clear and cutting. 'Especially when my heart was breaking. You mean you couldn't find sympathy, Anne, for a fourteen-year-old girl who was a stranger in your country and had just lost her beloved parents? God, you never cared about anyone or anything in your whole life but your rotten self.'

'Girls, girls!' Marcus's voice rose above Stephanie's. 'This is dreadful and I don't need it.'

'I'm sorry.' Stephanie shook her head and then looked at him subdued. 'Why do we all keep hurting each other? I don't want to hurt anyone.'

'Let's go home, Stephanie,' Marcus said finally.

'Take it!' Anne cried wildly. 'Take it. It's the only offer you're going to get.'

Stephanie didn't even stop to think or drop her eyes. 'No, Anne,' she said quietly, without triumph but a deep, certain knowledge.

For a moment Anne didn't even seem to hear her. She sat stiff and bloodless with a strange glow in her eyes then she seemed to explode into action. Something was lying near her foot, some small implement from the French marble mantle. She stooped over and picked it up, then in a stiffening fury lifted it above her head.

'Anne, you're mad. Totally mad!' Marcus called out in a great, anguished cry at the same time lifting his hands as though to protect his head.

But it was Stephanie Anne was after. She lifted

the brass implement in the shape of a small,
pierced spade higher above her head and came at
Stephanie like a madwoman, the exact opposite of
the coldly patrician creature she had enacted for
so long. Hatred and humiliation swamped every
last thought. She had always known, known, this
creature. . .

Stephanie was aware of odd little sounds like
whimpers. She knew they weren't coming from
her and Anne had her mouth set in a cruel, bright
line. She threw out her hand behind her knocking
over a small table, the lamp and a crystal bowl
filled with yellow roses. If she could only find the
poker they could fight a duel.

Anne's first blow hit the red velvet Louis chair,
at the same moment Marcus shrieked. His right
arm was still stabbing the air as though warding
off savage blows and a sweat had broken out on
his pale forehead. He wanted nothing more in the
world than to have the full use of his legs but he
was pinned to the chair.

'Lord, you're crazy!' Stephanie yelled as Anne
found yet another mark, the lovely old sconce on
the wall.

'We'll see if you can stay so pretty!' Anne took
another slashing step.

There was some terrific burst of sound behind
them and Stephanie wavered, half turning
towards it. It was Boyd, she realised, though she
had never seen him wearing that expression
before. It shocked her, the white-hot fury.

'Stephanie, look out!' He covered the distance
in record time but he was not near enough. With
one swift, convulsive blow Anne brought her
victim down.

Stephanie staggered slightly then fell, going

down in a rapidly darkening red haze while Anne, incredibly drew back, looking down at the weapon in her hand with boundless horror.

Boyd wrenched it off her and she looked up at him stupidly. 'She wouldn't . . . go . . . away.'

Boyd closed his hand on her shoulder and threw her aside. In one long terrible day this was the only moment he knew fear. Stephanie was lying on her side with golden roses scattered around her like . . . like. . . .

'Shut up, Marcus!' he turned and cried savagely and Marcus turned his moaning off like a light. After a lifetime of law and order, this!

Boyd was down on his knees beside Stephanie and as he very, very gently examined her head Ralph and Cathy burst through the door, their anxious faces going blank with horror.

It was at that very moment that, Anne, fantastically, began to laugh.

CHAPTER SEVEN

FOR six weeks or so after Stephanie had returned to Sydney, nothing seemed to matter. Not the fact that she and Marcus had parted with no love on either side, not his assuring her that under the circumstances she could scarcely continue working for him which meant she was out of a job, not the great good fortune that she was swept up by a rival agency within a couple of days. She had stormed off Opal like a heroine in a melodrama with those that loved her keeping a tight rein on their thoughts and opinions.

After all, who could forget the terrible way Anne had lashed out at her? Such a violent, passionate gesture. Only a miracle and a fairly poor aim had saved her from serious injury. The intent was still there. Even then she had nursed a cracked head for days. Harry and Ellen and Cath had circled her around, supportive and loving and bridling with indignation while Boyd loomed in doorways just managing to stay civil. It was one thing apparently to escape violent death himself and quite another to be involved in some sordid soap opera.

After Stephanie had fully recovered her health if not her temper, she and Boyd, in fact, had a blazing row. Stephanie didn't think she could ever forgive him for calling her an *idiot* ... *irresponsible* ... for having admitted anything to Anne. Didn't everyone know Anne was unhinged? he had hurled at her to which

Stephanie had cried: 'Then why didn't someone take her away?'

Anne went herself. One early morning by Jack Leonard's charter flight. She took some of her clothes and all of her jewellery. She left a note warning her husband that she was going to apply for an immediate divorce. A *coup de grâce* which her husband took very bravely. There seemed no reason now to hang on to a marriage when they hadn't embraced in years. Harry passed the interesting comment that it was 'the only intelligent thing left to do'. In fact everyone had a great deal to say, household and staff alike, except Boyd and Stephanie, who after their row didn't have a great deal left to say to each other.

Cath and the baby had seen her off with brimming eyes but Boyd had better things to do running the station. For which, Stephanie told herself and Cath, she was deeply grateful. A woman's intuition was to be taken very seriously. She had known all these years Anne was out to get her just as she had known she would finish up with Boyd's insults ringing in her ears. She couldn't even recall now he had ever offered to marry her. They were and always would be a fearful pair.

'A breathing space, a breathing space, that's what you need!' Harry had assured her, but Stephanie knew that she needed really hard work. Preferably of a manual nature. She even considered trying to get a job with a well-known horse trainer of her acquaintance. She rather fancied giving a thoroughbred a workout, but alas the trainer though diverted by the suggestion couldn't be persuaded. Women and horses didn't mix even if a woman jockey was victorious every other week.

So Stephanie took the first job, the only job, that was offered to her. She thought she would be compelled to suffer a reduction in salary and in the end nearly fainted at the sum that was mentioned. Another black mark against Marcus. She was even assigned one of the better offices, was not required to work excessive unpaid hours and was seldom harrassed by male attention. She was treated as a valuable, respected member of the staff. The only way she could respond was in winning good accounts. Preferably from Marcus.

Naturally the clients couldn't help hearing of the split. The news was well circulated, worked in as a bit of gossip, and gradually Stephanie began to pick up where she had left off. She was a very good-looking girl which always helped and she had flair. She lost herself in her job and became so good at it Marcus of all people rang her to ask her out for a drink. Imagine! Stephanie didn't slam the phone down in his ear which he deserved, but she did get in a few, very-sure-of-herself sarcastic remarks.

Marcus however was waiting for her outside the building as she left work.

'Please, please, Stephanie. Is it too much to ask?' He looked very elegant and gleaming. Back to his old self.

'You've got a nerve, Marcus,' she returned coolly.

'I had to, Stephanie. You see that?'

'I think you enjoyed kicking me out.'

'There will never be anyone like you, Stephanie.' He put his hand on her arm.

'I hear you and Raina Simmons are going lots of places together.'

'What do you care?' Marcus turned her in the direction of his favourite bar.

'Her father's got millions. What more do you want?'

'She's a fantastic girl.' Marcus's smooth face showed just a hint of greedy triumph.

'You know it will be marriage, Marcus, don't you?' she lightly taunted him. 'No hanky panky with Russ Simmon's girl. You'll be respectable at last.'

'And what about you?' Marcus led her downstairs into the softly lit interior.

'I've met all the wrong men.'

Habits are of long standing. Quite unconsciously they sought a familiar table and an equally familiar waiter came over to take their order.

'What happened on Opal after I left?' Marcus asked darkly.

'It was fairly peaceful,' Stephanie joked. The demands that she made upon herself had caused her to lose several pounds in weight and she looked model-girl thin, more glossily beautiful but without the radiance of the old days.

'You look marvellous!' Marcus breathed, trying to look into her eyes. She was wearing more make-up than she used to, expertly applied, and those violet eyes were huge, surrounded by an extravagant sweep of thick, silky lashes. He loved her silk blouse though her breasts were slighter. What an asset she could have been to him. Could still be if only, if only. . . .

'Don't look at me like that, Marcus,' she warned him. 'You can't do as you like now, you know.'

'We had something wonderful together,' he told her.

'You mean you had a top business colleague.'

'Which brings me to what I wanted to discuss.' He leaned back as the waiter arrived with their drinks. 'Thank you.' Marcus left a small tip, which caused Stephanie to smile. Smile or explode with indignation. How Marcus had underpaid her, making up for it with charm.

'The whole team is missing you.' He leaned forward now showing his good teeth in his best smile.

'Not old Howie?' Stephanie asked.

'Everyone.' Marcus squeezed her hand. 'You were far and away our favourite.'

'Favourite dogsbody,' Stephanie returned pleasantly. 'What a simple little soul I was, but it takes time to work things out.'

'Just so.' Marcus nodded impressively. 'Come back to us, Steph. I'll make it worth your while.'

'How much?' Following his lead, Stephanie took a gulp of her drink.

'We can't settle things right now.'

'Why ever not?' Professional people went by, acquaintances, and Stephanie and Marcus smiled at them. Marcus like the cat who inevitably deserved the cream. 'I'm listening, Marcus,' Stephanie said.

He named an excellent figure. For him.

Stephanie yawned.

'Don't tell me Chapman is paying you more than that?'

'From the beginning.'

'I don't believe it.'

'You wouldn't.' She took a deep breath. 'I'm happy where I am, Marcus. I get a warm feeling when I walk inside the door. I'm moving along quickly too.'

'So I heard,' Marcus murmured rather sourly. 'Guess who I saw the other day?'

'Man, woman?' Not very seriously Stephanie met his eyes. In another few moments she would get up and leave.

'Woman. That very strange woman, Anne Ballinger.'

'My God!' Stephanie actually shuddered. 'I can't believe you stopped.'

'She stopped me.'

'What with? Some great mastiff?'

'She acted as though absolutely nothing had happened,' Marcus confided wryly.

'They usually do,' Stephanie remarked grimly.

'No, seriously, she seemed perfectly normal. I had a friend with me and he thought she was very attractive.'

'If he is a friend you'd be doing him a kindness steering him away.'

'She's left her husband, of course. As it happened my friend had to go off so Anne and I shared a cup of coffee.'

'Oh, no!' Stephanie rolled her eyes.

'She bitterly regrets what she did.'

'I think she'd do it again.'

'I felt sorry for her in a way.'

'Don't,' Stephanie warned. 'You said it the first time. She's a very strange woman.'

'She couldn't understand why you lied to her,' Marcus said.

'About what?' Stephanie said so sharply one or two heads turned.

'About Ballinger asking you to marry him. Of course I knew it was fantasy.'

'One or two things have quite put me off marriage,' Stephanie said.

'You'll get over him,' Marcus said. 'I don't want to give you any more disagreeable news but Anne said he seems to have picked out his future bride. She said you might know her. Laura Clifford?'

Nothing. Absolutely nothing had hit her so hard. Not even Anne. Laura Clifford. Stephanie recalled her in a flash. Nearer Boyd's age. Late twenties. A tall, lovely blonde. Marvellous honey-gold hair. Rich, pastoral family. Why should it be such a surprise?

'Say something, Stephanie,' Marcus's voice came to her.

Stephanie managed a valiant laugh and Marcus laughed in relief with her. 'She's a lovely girl. I remember her quite well. Another one who always followed Boyd around. I can't quite fit in where she came. There were so many on the scene. I know she stayed on Opal several times. She was quite friendly with Boyd's other sister.'

'Maybe you can forget him now,' Marcus said.

'I suppose I'll have to.' She was trying to joke but she had gone very pale.

'You really love him, don't you?' Marcus offered bleakly.

'Sure I love him!' There were suddenly tears in her eyes. 'It's a dreadful affliction like asthma. Mostly incurable. You wake up one morning and you've got it and it never goes away.'

'It must be very difficult to live with,' Marcus said.

'Hell when I'm not working very hard.'

'And he played on your affections,' Marcus said harshly. 'Broke your heart.'

'No, I think he just got tired of me,' Stephanie gave a little shuddering sigh.

'Tired of you! What does that mean?' Marcus asked crisply.

'Who cares right now,' Stephanie said. 'Obviously he's consoling himself with someone a whole lot more stable, the skunk!' She could feel a tight band gathering around her chest. She couldn't bear it. One didn't refuse Boyd Ballinger. Or rather not have the common decency to put her refusal into words. That blow on the head must have made her crazy.

'Do you want another drink?' Rather feverishly Marcus signalled the waiter.

'I want to go home.' Stephanie said. 'Clever old Anne spilling all the gossip over coffee.'

'She seemed rather happy about it,' Marcus said.

'I don't . . . believe . . . it,' Stephanie hesitated. 'The only time Anne is happy is when she's making trouble.'

'Oh, for God's sake, Steph,' Marcus cried impatiently, 'he's got to marry somebody.'

'When he asked me I didn't think he had anyone else in mind.'

'You mean he did ask you,' Marcus said flatly.

'I sure don't know why but he did.'

'Then he must love you,' Marcus said bitterly. 'A man like that doesn't go around asking women to marry him. For God's sake, Stephanie, isn't that what you wanted? Are you out of your mind?'

'If Cath asks me to the wedding I'll have to go in a straitjacket.

'I doubt if they'll ask you,' Marcus returned acidly. 'You mean you turned him down? You need help.'

'Don't laugh at me, Marcus,' she said quietly,

'but I've always had this terrible fear I'll lose those I love.'

'My dear!' Something in her tone struck at Marcus's fairly stony heart. In view of the fact she had lost her parents so tragically and at such an age he didn't find such a deep-seated anxiety unreasonable. 'I understand, of course. But one must be prepared to face life.'

'I see that now.'

'You mean you gave up Ballinger because you thought that one day you might lose him?'

'I wanted to run away from how much I love him. Crazy isn't it?' She smiled through a shimmer of tears.

'Did you explain that to him?'

'I don't have to explain things to Boyd.' Stephanie wrapped her shaky hand around her empty glass. 'He knows all about me.'

'My dear you could have had treatment. These anxieties can be helped.'

'Hearing he's going to marry someone else has cured me on the spot.'

'I'm sorry, Stephanie,' Marcus said. 'Look, why don't we have dinner, for old times' sake?'

Stephanie went straight home, feeling unbelievably shaken. The one thing she hadn't foreseen was Boyd's getting over her so quickly. She could even begin to forget about him. But then she was a woman. Love, the absence of it was always gnawing away at a woman but men seemed to have some new mountain to climb. So he could do without her? She knew she couldn't do without him. Even her success in business couldn't balance the flat emptiness in her life. She had been trying to guard her peace of mind too well. In refusing the risks of loving she could very well end up a zombie. Nothing lost, nothing gained. Nothing.

There was mail waiting for her. No bills, a rarity. Two invitations to art showings at rival galleries. Her favourite boutique was having a sale. A letter from Ellen. Ellen always addressed the envelope though word from both of them was always inside and marvel of marvels a letter, or rather a short gracious note from Boyd's mother.

Stephanie read, then reread it, then turned it over and read it again. Could Stephanie please give her the pleasure of her company at a Ballinger get-together at the end of the month? It was a long weekend and anticipating Stephanie's acceptance Elizabeth had booked flights for her which tied up with a charter flight to the station. All Stephanie had to do was pack a few things, including a pretty dress, and wangle the Friday off. If she could manage Tuesday, so much the better. Elizabeth would love to see her. She had always considered Stephanie somehow part of the family.

Stephanie couldn't seem to deal with the unexpectedness of it. The short letter was just as nice as it could have been. A woman like Elizabeth could never do anything so devastating as invite Stephanie to her son's surprise engagement party. If Cath had seen how Stephanie felt about Boyd could anyone be more observant than a mother? No, it had to be something else. Maybe Mark was getting engaged. But why didn't they say?

Ellen didn't say either. If Elizabeth wanted to arrange a get-together for family and old friends who were mere mortals to question it? Stephanie knew, though she felt desperately at sea, she would go. She jumped up and looked in the mirror. She looked a wreck. How odd, she hadn't noticed she was too thin. At her best she was every bit as good-looking as Laura Clifford. Heavens, she looked better. But looks weren't everything. One had to display a willingness for total commitment. She wasn't even worried about that any more. All she was worried about was Laura Clifford with the lovely, honey-coloured hair. Laura had no fears. She had led a charmed life. Lucky Laura. Stephanie crossed herself.

Her boss told her cheerfully certainly she could take Friday off and Tuesday and Wednesday as well if she could land a certain fashion account. No one had ever seen Stephanie move so fast. The ideas flowed from her, the outline of a winning campaign. For a fortnight she was sure she could sell sand at Ayers Rock so that her boss beamed on her and every day their client took them out to lunch.

Stephanie gained her few pounds and some stunning additions to her wardrobe. By the time the Friday of her departure came she felt so buoyant she thought there wasn't a man alive who could get away from her if she wanted him. She didn't even give Laura Clifford a sporting chance.

It was a long flight requiring two changes but Stephanie passed the time chatting to the person who sat next to her between bouts of relaxation when she lounged with her head back and eyes closed. She had been away from Boyd for a few months yet she hadn't been away at all. He always came to her at night when her dreams unlocked her subconscious. The lover she longed for.

There was a wait at Emerald for the charter plane and when Stephanie boarded she turned to face a half a dozen people she knew. Outback people and long-time Ballinger friends. It was good to see them and they accepted her presence as naturally as they had accepted their own invitations. Elizabeth came too infrequently to Opal these days so every visit was precious. They would all have a good time and maybe do a little business as well.

A lot of talk and laughter passed to and fro but Stephanie never heard a single thing that could possibly worry her. Surely if Boyd had picked up his old friendship with Laura Clifford all these people would know. Precious few secrets escaped the two-way radio. Almost from the beginning of white settlement the Outback had been one large extended family.

'We're coming in over Opal now,' their pilot announced and Stephanie sat forward and stared out the window.

'There, doesn't that look grand!' the head of the Drummond clan breathed in her ear. 'I've always had a special feeling about this place. The people on it. Boyd's father was my best friend. I can remember the day he left us. I'd never heard worse news in my life. Still, he left sons. Boyd will keep the station intact.'

And so they flew in to the very heart of the vast station and stockmen on the property took off their slouch hats and waved. It was always the same when Elizabeth arrived. A softness fell on the place. A memory of what it was. Opal needed a mistress.

Station vehicles were standing by to drive them all up to the homestead and when they arrived

Elizabeth was there to meet them, flanked by her two daughters, Julia and Cath. Husbands were hovering in the background, but it was Elizabeth's moment.

Stephanie allowed the older guests to precede her, her eyes travelling over Elizabeth's so particularly endearing face. She was more elegantly turned out than Stephanie had ever yet seen her, quite obviously still in her city image and a few of the ladies were eyeing her stunning, mature beauty, the marvellous clothes and the elegantly shod feet, with a slight wariness. Could their Elizabeth have changed?

Then Elizabeth laughed, a warm gust and it reminded them all vividly of the way things had been. Heavens, she hadn't changed a bit. They weren't going to be taken in by that slick city gear. Julia, too, looked magnificent, black hair, white skin, the fantastic Ballinger eyes though they had a somewhat steely cast. She looked highly intelligent as well which she was but she had quite missed out on the delightful qualities of her mother. Where Julia was formidable, Elizabeth drew people with her genuine warmth. Besides these two splendid creatures tawny little Cath looked no more than a schoolgirl. She even stood a little back from them by instinct, but as soon as she saw Stephanie smiling and waving to her, her eyes flashed and her wide sensitive mouth curved up in a huge, answering smile.

Then it was Stephanie's turn.

'Good Lord I would never have known you, Stephanie!' Julia almost frowned.

'But, my dear, Stephanie never changes!' Elizabeth put her arm around Stephanie and kissed her cheek, her eyes moving with the greatest satisfaction over Stephanie's lovely fine-boned face and slender body. There were no travel smudges beneath her eyes, no creases in her beautifully cut linen trousers caught with a stylish belt, nor on the black-and-white silk crepe de Chine shirt with its matching scarf. She looked perfect, easy and uncontrived.

They talked for a few moments, almost avidly, there was so much to catch up on then Elizabeth hugged her again and promised 'a private session'.

'Your mother looks wonderful!' Stephanie said, as Cath half floated with her up the stairs.

'Doesn't she, beautiful creature. Oh, it's lovely to be home together!'

'I've missed you,' Stephanie said. 'And how's the little man?'

'Bigger. A whole lot bigger. He's asleep at the moment. The flight upset him a little.'

Cath stayed with her while she unpacked, snatching up this or that to say how gorgeous it was. 'Heavens, did you see Julia's face when she saw you?'

'She did seem surprised,' Stephanie murmured. She would always be close to Cath but she doubted if she and Julia could ever get together.

'Of course you look a knock-out,' Cath said proudly. 'Julia may be very beautiful but she doesn't like anybody, except perhaps Mummy, to look better than she.'

'And I look better?' Stephanie chuckled.

'My goodness, of course you do!' Cathy confirmed explosively. 'You don't imagine for one moment Julia is more attractive than you. A woman has to be able to draw people. I'm afraid my big sister doesn't do that,' Cath added candidly.

'Her husband is here, of course. I thought I saw him with Jim?'

'I think they decided not to intrude on the welcome. It's Mummy's moment. You'll be seeing them when we all come together for a pre-dinner drink. He's not a bad bloke. A bit stuffy and pompous. I don't think he knows how to unwind. Any more than Julia.'

'And Mark and Ralph?'

'They're both fine,' Cath smiled. 'You'd hardly know Uncle Ralph these days. He's doing a lot of things he's never done before. Deputising for Boyd here, there and everywhere. It's Boyd, of course, keeping him on the move. There was a time Uncle Ralph never dared to make a decision without first consulting Daddy then Boyd, now Boyd has told him plainly he's got every confidence in him so why shouldn't he have it in himself. It seems to be the best therapy in the world. That and being free of . . . Anne.'

'I'm told she's a new woman as well,' Stephanie managed that without any harshness. 'Marcus saw her one day.'

'Great Scott!' Cath looked shocked. 'Don't tell me he stopped to chat?'

'Uuum, they did. Over a cup of coffee.' Stephanie shut the bureau drawer.

'Good grief, didn't he think she was trying to kill him the last time?'

'No hard feelings as far as Marcus is concerned.' Stephanie's eyes were very large and brilliant. 'She said also Boyd is seeing a lot of. . . .'

'Laura Clifford.'

'Oh, God, is he?' Stephanie groaned. She who had been looking so beautiful and vivid suddenly crumpled beside Cath on the four poster.

'I don't know actually what's going on,' Cath looked deeply embarrassed. 'I have an idea she's been invited.'

'Really?'

'I'm afraid so,' Cath said falteringly. 'Boyd won't talk to anyone about his affairs.'

'I thought he talked to you.' Stephanie could almost hear the accusation in her own voice. 'Oh, Cath, what am I to do?'

'But you told him, dearest, you wouldn't marry him.'

'I never did.'

'Oh!' Cath stared at her friend fascinated. 'I thought you did.'

'I never actually said anything. We just traded insults. I never said, for instance, I won't marry you. I just told him he was the most arrogant man on earth.'

'Oh, Stephy!'

'Why not? He swore at me.'

'Boyd did?'

'He called me a silly little bitch. Half-witted like the rest of my sex.'

'Oh, that was only talk,' Cath breathed in relief. 'He really admires you. The way you've made such a success of yourself.'

'It didn't take him too long to forget me, did it?' To cover her feelings Stephanie jumped up off the bed and of all things began to vigorously brush her hair.

'Why, he hasn't forgotten you, Stephy. Don't get upset.'

'Is he serious about Laura?' Now Stephanie's oval face was surrounded by a magnificent mass of curls.

'Honestly, I know nothing!' Cath's eyes dropped. 'My best advice to you is don't let it happen. You were his first choice. I would have thought his only choice. He's expected to get married, you know. He can't hang about much longer for a wife. I guess you'll have to make a decision, Stephy. Do you want him or not?'

'Oh, I do!' Stephanie joined her hands together in an attitude of prayer.

'Marriage, we're talking about, Stephanie,' Cath said very firmly.

'What else?' Stephanie blinked at her.

'There now, I was only testing you,' Cath said in a quite different voice. 'What are you wearing tonight?'

'What do you suggest? Demure or daring?'

'Oh, daring every time. Laura is lovely, but she's the least bit dull.'

'I had the impression Boyd was tired of volatile women,' Stephanie shot back. 'I wonder when Harry and Ellen will arrive?'

'Oh, Boyd has gone for them,' Cath offered casually. 'The Gunderson's are flying in tomorrow morning so we should have a full roll-call by then. About forty people in all. The boys have a few things organised. A spot of polo. They never miss an opportunity. We girls might have to natter a bit unless you're bold enough to want to take out a motorcycle?'

'You're joking!'

'No. Jim taught me. It's fantastic!'

In the meantime other guests were arriving, little Peter woke up and wanted his mother, then Harry and Ellen were standing outside Stephanie's door.

'Darlings!' Stephanie couldn't get to them

quick enough and they hurried towards her so in the end the three of them all but crashed.

'Marvellous ... marvellous ... isn't she marvellous,' Harry glanced at Ellen who as the smallest was getting knocked about a bit.

'Oh, how I've missed you!'

'You're standing on my foot, Harry,' Ellen broke in quickly.

'Then break loose, dear one. You're such a little thing.'

'Oh, I've missed you,' Stephanie repeated. 'I think the greatest part of my life is coming out here. It must be where I belong.'

'I think so,' Ellen said promptly, then seized by an answering bout of affection clasped Stephanie to her.

By seven in the evening the guests were beginning to go downstairs. The great house looked magical and Stephanie reflected as she descended the staircase how much difference a woman, the right woman, made. Elizabeth had only been in residence a few days yet the house had responded to her presence like flowers to water. Indeed flowers were used as never before, introducing their scent and their lovely living aura so that the imposing aspect of the huge entrance hall and reception rooms was played down. The immense chandeliers were blazing, every door was thrown open and the many lamps turned on. It looked very beautiful and grand but more importantly welcoming. It looked a home.

Stephanie moved very slowly, catching the sounds of talk and laughter, orchestral music playing quietly. Her mind strayed back to the first time she had ever come to this house. She had never known people so rich or anyone who lived in a house that was so big. To her fourteen-year-old eyes it had seemed like a palace and there could never have been a more devastating prince. She thought of Cath's twenty-first birthday party, Anne Ballinger, but refused to dwell on it. That was in the past. Could there be any more terrible weapons than ridicule and spite? Some women lived by venom and others lived for love and friendship. The thing was, one had to embrace life. She saw that now.

As she neared the marble floor of the entrance hall a man emerged from the drawing room, a smile on his face that disappeared as soon as he looked up and saw Stephanie poised a few feet above him.

'Boyd?' Somehow she found herself stretching out her hand. Her expression was very soft and faintly startled, her violet eyes startling in the depth of their colour. She was wearing a simple but very sophisticated dress in a beautiful bois de rose and to compliment its very narrow, clinging lines she had faintly teased sections of her gleaming, dark-mahogany hair. Parted in the centre it stood away from the fine bones of her face and cascaded in glossy waves and curls just past her shoulders. She had never looked better, but now when she needed it, it gave her little confidence.

There was that brilliant glitter to his eyes, the haughty, aristocratic look that Julia wielded so well. He was not going to be so easily placated but if he was deeply disturbed as she was, he wasn't showing it.

'Please. Pax. Peace.' Her lovely smile was a little twisted.

'Stephanie,' he moved at last, accepting her hand, that despite her wishes trembled, perhaps softening him so as he stood on the stair below her he only had to move his head a little to kiss her cheek. 'My, my, you do look beautiful!' It was mocking but it sounded genuine as well.

'You look beautiful too,' she told him.

'How sweet of you to say so.' He still held her hand. 'And how truly sweet of you to accept my mother's invitation. We all do appreciate it.'

'Come on, now,' she said gently, 'don't be angry with me.'

'My darling girl I refuse to get steamed up about you at all.'

Nevertheless they were so focused on each other they failed to notice the young woman who had followed Boyd out into the hall and was now staring at them with enormous interest.

'Oh, Laura,' Boyd said and drew Stephanie down the remaining stairs. 'I'm sure you remember Stephanie Sinclair, don't you?'

'Why of course I do!' Laura came forward, only friendliness in her manner. 'How are you, Stephanie? It must be four or five years?'

'And you look lovelier than ever, Laura.' One had to say it, it was quite true.

'Thank you.' Laura gave a luminous smile. 'That applies equally well to you. You've grown up, Stephanie, in a few short years.'

Boyd appeared unimpressed by that but Laura was obviously sincere. 'Julia was telling me you're doing extremely well in the advertising world.'

Julia was? How extraordinary. Laura took Stephanie's arm as though they had been close friends for years and Boyd glanced down on them both. 'I'll have to disappear for a few minutes. An important business call. Go into the library. Everyone seems to be gathering there.'

'No wonder!' Laura carolled. 'It's a marvellous room.'

Stephanie didn't know how she was going to react to Laura. She was not accustomed to disliking people and she found she couldn't start now. Laura had a lovely appearance and a lovely manner. My God, Stephanie thought. Truly she would make a wonderful wife and hostess. She had an air of quality and a genuine liking for her fellow man. And woman. Nothing bitchy about Laura. She presented the image she really was.

'How nice to meet you,' Stephanie said to this one and that. She was not sure Julia's husband was as stuffy as he looked, some spark in the eye: Cath's husband Jim was as nice as ever; because he was sitting in judgment on an important case Elizabeth's husband was not able to be present. She had never encountered Julia's brother-in-law, Richard, who had been invited along for some reason and it struck her how much more attractive he was than his older brother. A far more pleasing personality as well. It was obvious too he and Laura were old friends, chatting comfortably and moving from one group to the other.

Stephanie held Mark Ballinger's girlfriend's hand, smiled into the green, gold-flecked eyes. 'Come and meet my sister,' Paula said.

It was difficult not to unwind. Harry was in his element like an actor on a stage. For a man who positively shone at parties it was quite extraordinary he had chosen to live his life in great solitude. Except for his perfect Ellen. Ellen had a new dress, Stephanie noted, a grey silk and for this very special occasion she had put on her pearls. Whatever else Ellen had sold, the pearls remained. They were family pearls, quite valuable and looked it, and they were to go to Stephanie. Ellen's gift.

For tonight the formal dining room had been opened up, the highly polished surface of the mahogany table reflecting the glitter of silver and crystal, the delicacy of the lace placemats, the rich blush of the flowers, the sparkle of bone china decorated and rimmed in gold.

Elizabeth sat at one end of the long darkly gleaming table, Boyd at the other and so sparkling were their glances at one another their love and pride in each other reached out to everyone. Stephanie had the feeling no matter what happened she would remember this evening with great tenderness. She heard Ralph Ballinger's voice a few places up, the echo of laughter in it and she stared across at the woman who was now challenging him with some spirit. Mrs Cameron, of course. Donald Cameron's widow. He had been struck down by a heart attack at the very early age of forty-seven. Louisa Cameron was a very brave and capable woman, much respected in the North. She still ran a very big station, though it was common knowledge she worked much too hard. Louisa Cameron was one of the Ballinger favourites.

The leisurely meal was superb starting with a nage of fresh seafood with Chablis and butter sauce, followed by roast fillet of Opal beef with a madeira demi-glaze and a wide selection of vegetables, cheese before the sweet to finish off the superb dry reds and for those who could still find a place, Pavarotti's sumptuous chocolate and raspberry cake especially created to honour the great tenor on his last visit to Australia. Stephanie had already sampled a few attempts at the original and this surely had to come close. Maybe even better. No one thought to resist it, though several mentioned they might stagger around the main compound before retiring on such a magnificent meal.

In actual fact no one seemed to think of retiring either. They were all enjoying themselves far too much. Stephanie saw that Laura often spoke to Julia and her party and she remembered now that Laura had gone to the same boarding school as Julia though Julia was a little older. Laura did have a lot of charm for Julia often smiled at her. Laura would be a smash-hit as a sister-in-law.

Stephanie glanced away from Laura and found Boyd's eyes hard on her. She knew that she flushed and hated herself for her transparency. There was a faintly satanic cast to his handsome features as he looked at her and her burning cheeks and she thought she could even hear what he was thinking: 'How long did you think I was going to wait, you little fool!'

A few minutes later she saw Laura take his arm in a very symbolic gesture of ownership. Women liked to let everyone know who was their man.

'Stephanie? Come back here this minute!' Elizabeth ordered laughingly. 'Harry is trying to make us swallow the most unlikely tale.'

It was a pleasure and a torment: sights and sounds and images, much laughter and more talk, a good deal of masculine attention to bolster her ego though she never cared much about egos.

Still she had to play a part; the part of a much-valued and cared-for family friend. Even Julia unbent and met her more than half way. Laura, amazingly, had quite taken to her. That more than anything almost broke her up. Still, she recovered enough to give the vivid impression of a party girl having a good time. It was beginning to make her very tired.

Incredibly there were those relatively untouched by the mountain of food they had consumed at dinner and backed up for a late supper. Elizabeth smiled at them all very kindly, much as an Edwardian hostess at one of those fabulous houseparties might have smiled on dear friends. There was no need to be embarrassed and as most of her guests were actively involved in outdoor pursuits, an extra kilo or two could scarcely matter.

Stephanie declined anything but a coffee and she really didn't want that. From vivacious she was going to slightly moody. A further digression might become a cause for concern. Meanwhile Boyd was the perfect host, circulating constantly but by some clever piece of strategy never standing beside Stephanie for more than five minutes. So much had happened to him since she had run away from Opal. Perhaps a spot of common sense. What sensible man could continue to hunger after a female who was forever running scared.

Towards twoish Stephanie wandered out on to the terrace in search of Elizabeth to calmly excuse herself, when she had to draw back in shock. Even her eyes were lacerated, and of a sudden she felt terribly ill. To her everlasting credit she never made a sound though her pallor showed when finally she caught up with her hostess. Half of the guests had drifted off and Elizabeth observed, as she touched Stephanie's cheek tenderly, she did look a little tired. 'All that travelling,' she realised. After that, Stephanie said her 'goodnights' very quickly, which was to say it was the end of the party so far as she was concerned even if they were well into morning. She wanted to be alone and alone was the word for it. She had not intercepted a passionate kiss but she thought she could quite fairly call it, deeply affectionate. Laura was the sort of wife who could make a considerable contribution to her marriage. She could handle everything that being mistress of Opal entailed. She was on excellent terms with Elizabeth and the girls. She was of an age to be very keen on settling down. She seemed too overwhelmingly right. Even I like her, Stephanie thought with a rush of sad astonishment. For God's sake, Laura was made for the job.

She pulled off her dress so hurriedly she looked down at it aghast. Some of the stitching had broken loose. She hung it away in the huge armoire and slipped her robe off its hangar, thoughts tumbling and tossing in her mind. This time she couldn't run away. She had to stand and face it. And I'll do it, she thought fiercely. God knows how, but I will.

She took off the rest of her clothes then belted herself into her silk robe, tying without even knowing she was doing it, a pretty silk knot. The robe was new, sheer luxury. One could have worn it downstairs but Stephanie didn't feel tempted to go downstairs again. Through these hours she would have to build some kind of barricade to get

her through the next few days. Boyd had settled
on a wife just as Cath had warned her. *And I
brought it all on myself*, she thought wryly. No
matter what animal instincts she aroused in Boyd,
he knew now it wouldn't work. Laura was a
woman of his own calibre. *Serves you right*,
Stephanie thought, her eyes stinging. *I'm learning*.
It was just that one only had one chance at a man
like Boyd in a lifetime. And if that wasn't bad
enough she was certain Harry and Ellen would
agree she had acted like a perfect idiot.

Still he could have told her, she thought
violently. Dropped some hint. Surely he owed
her that much? She could hardly blame Boyd for
her broken engagement. She had contrived that
little misadventure all by herself but it was Boyd
who had caused her to look at Marcus with fresh
eyes. He had to take a measure of the blame. She
didn't know it, but she was whipping herself up
into a temper. Expecting fidelity from a man was
all too much. She didn't want to think about her
own rapid defection from a man she had briefly
become engaged to. For one thing Marcus could
look after himself. It was Boyd who was the
villain. She had only to turn her back on him to
be instantly supplanted. She had never felt so
angry and miserable at once.

She thought the first tap on her door was a
figment of her overwrought imagination but it
came again. Goodness it wasn't that Ivor
Patterson surely. He had insisted she was the
most beautiful creature he had ever seen and she
had played up to him once or twice. The brief
moments when Boyd had been within earshot. If
this was Ivor he must have taken leave of his
senses or her few pleasantries had raised his

expectations astronomically high. She comforted
herself she could deal very well with the
situation. Years of being a working girl had
taught her that.

She rather threw open her door with a very
brisk, aggressive expression that immediately
turned to upset.

'What the devil are you doing here?' she
demanded shortly.

'It's my house.'

'There's no reason why you should come in.'
She thrust her head around the door so she could
look up and down the corridor.

'Please, Stephanie,' he said sardonically, 'don't
let anyone catch us like this .'

'I'm warning you. . . .'

'Oh, shut up.' His voice held a drawling
sarcasm that incited her to rage.

'Your house or not. . . .'

He caught her around the waist and pushed her
through the door. 'Why is it as soon as I get near
you I feel violent?'

'How dare you come in here, Boyd?' she lashed
at him. 'Surely this is the last thing you want?'

'Never,' he said and looked down at her. 'And
no pretended maidenly outrage either. I was
coming to you or you were coming to me. Which
was it going to be?'

'What kind of fool game are you playing now?'
she demanded. 'You've been avoiding me all
night.'

'And haven't you taken it to heart!' His silver
eyes were sparkling like diamonds.

'Why not?' Her face flushed hotly. 'When I
think of the fool you've made of me.'

To her amazement, he laughed. Not a light,

amused laugh, more like a playful growl. 'It did teach you a thing or two.'

'Such as?'

'I want to take you to bed,' he said, a few hard edges to the soft mockery. Had he been drinking too much? He looked just the same. All vivid, male arrogance.

'The chances you take,' she said bleakly, 'or do you think you can get away with everything?'

'Who's to know if you don't scream?' He put his arm around her and drew her to him. 'You look fabulous tonight. I loved your dress, but this is even better.'

'I'll tell your mother,' she threatened.

'I'm sure she knows.' Those gleaming eyes taunted her.

'And then you're going to get married?' she cried incredulously.

'Why not?' He held her tighter, his fingers spearing into the thick masses of her hair.

'You b-bast——'

He didn't give her a chance to finish, his mouth catching hers up with such mastery, it treacherously opened to that inflammatory assault. She thought she should have willingly flung herself out the window to avoid such a shockingly easy conquest but he was holding her so powerfully, forcing her head back, she felt drowned in a sensual storm.

How many times have I imagined this, she thought ravenously while he continued to plunder her mouth with a passion that had a touch of studied cruelty.

Finally she was able to make a little moaning protest trying to turn her neck. 'You're hurting me, you big, strong brute!'

'Hush, Stephanie,' he murmured warningly, 'if we keep our voices down no one will ever know we're here.'

'Oh, won't they?' She was so furious at his insolence she even tried to bite him.

'How very wild of you, Stephanie!' He rubbed at the spot with an answering wildness in his handsome, dark face.

'Don't think you're going to have me!' she exclaimed proudly.

'I am. And very slowly.' His sparkling eyes swept over her, the curl of derision on his sculptured mouth. 'If you don't want to get hurt, don't use your teeth or your nails. At least, not hard.'

'This is a bit feudal, isn't it?' she said cuttingly, 'Perhaps it's a bit too isolated here. Haven't you heard there's a women's movement going on?'

'In a lot of things they don't change.' Just to prove it he was studying her in much the same fashion a feudal lord might have studied the village maiden he meant to ravish.

'Except I don't desire you.'

'Then why have your eyes gone purple? I can show you a mirror if you like.'

He did so and she was shocked at the change in herself. She looked deliberately, wildly, provocative, the mane of her hair almost feline, a high colour deepening the natural gold of her skin, her eyes narrowed and yes, a deep purple, the neck of her robe thrown back to reveal the rising curves of her breasts. It was strange to see herself as a temptress but this time she had to find the strength to withstand her own longings. A small-scale death before dishonour.

'Looked enough?' He brushed her hair aside

and kissed her neck and she nearly melted back against him.

'What am I supposed to be?' she asked a little brokenly, 'a sex object?'

'I can't think of anyone better.' He brought his hands up over her slender, flushed body, caressing her breasts with his palms, his thumbs brushing back and forth against her highly sensitive erect nipples.

'Oh . . . Boyd . . . please . . . stop.'

'I can't, darling,' his voice was harsh and urgent. 'There's always the point when you can't stop.'

'But why are you doing this?' Her head fell back against his shoulder so he could kiss her mouth.

'To show you how much I want you.'

'You're crazy!' she gasped as his mouth rose just fractionally. 'What about Laura?'

'Laura can do as she likes.'

'What?' She spun around as though she could hardly believe her ears.

'Damn it, don't let's talk about Laura,' he gritted. 'Especially after you've been away from me for months!' He almost jolted her back into his arms, on his face such an expression of unbridled arrogance her hand came up to slap him.

'Don't.'

'You can't make me,' she said. 'I'm not going to be your . . . mistress,' she hissed furiously.

'You'll be anything I choose.' He caught her up fiercely, carrying her back to the bed and throwing her right into the middle of it. She had always said he looked like a fallen angel now the devilish side was coming out.

'Talk about arrogance!' She sat up swiftly with fire in her eyes. 'Why don't you try playing the gentleman for a change?'

'I did, for what it was worth.' He moved on to the bed beside her, his eyes dwelling with overpowering sensuality on her near naked breasts. 'You must think seriously, Stephanie, about taking a lover. After all, you're nearly twenty-four and as far as that goes a decided exception to the rule.'

'There ought to be more like me!' she cried, trying to cover herself more modestly but with one lithe-bodied movement he had her back on the bed, ignoring her gallant resistance, lifting her almost roughly until she was pressed wantonly against him with only the clinging silk between them.

'Can't you understand I hate this!' Even as she was saying it her mouth was reaching blindly for his.

'Darling, Stephanie, don't fight me.'

She didn't want that deep tenderness. Not now. Not when she was trying dazedly to remember harsh reality. Where was her pride? For that matter where was honour? How could he kiss her in such a sweetly savage way? Nothing, absolutely nothing made sense.

'Stephanie, Stephanie . . .!'

He had her shuddering in a near agony, every nerve in her body sensitive to his touch.

'All you have to do is love me.'

'But I do love you,' she cried. 'I do love you. I do.' Tears were flowing from her drowned eyes. 'What a swine you are.'

'Why, baby?' Belatedly he decided to be gentle, turning her stricken face and covering it in nibbling little kisses.

'What about Laura?' she cried in a passion of self-disgust.

Unexpectedly, shockingly, he laughed, lying back on the bed and slipping an arm behind his curling, raven head. 'Laura has been keeping company for at least a year. Or so they tell me.'

'Really?' She sat up staring down at him frowningly. 'But you've eliminated him, of course?'

'Why ever would I wish to do that?' he looked back at her calmly. 'What is this about Laura? She's certainly not in the forefront of my mind.'

'You mean you're not going to marry her?' So Anne was a pathological liar, Cath had thought him quite serious. Why that tender kiss?

'At one time she was a contender, of course.' He put out his hand and began caressing her breast.

'Stop that!' she said furiously.

'I thought you liked it?' he gave her a hard smile.

'I was told that you were going to marry Laura,' she said.

'And that annoyed you?' Despite her explosive protest he resumed caressing her body.

'Who got this story going?' She tried to lift herself away.

'I have no idea. What beautiful skin you have, darling. You're so delicious I could eat you.' He lifted his head and put his mouth to her breast and she had to moan aloud.

'Please, Boyd. Please talk to me.'

'All right.' He lay back and pulled her down beside him, sliding his arm under her so she had to lie along the length of his body. 'There was a need to bring you to your senses, you will admit?'

'You mean this was some kind of plan?' she demanded in shock but he kept her down.

'No, not really. At least not at the beginning. But some rumour went around. I don't think we need to do much guessing about who started it so I thought it wouldn't exactly hurt you to have a hard time.'

'You what?' She couldn't even prop herself up on her elbow.

'Lie still.' His arm tightened around her slender, soft body. 'I think you thought I was going to wait forever?'

'You did this to me on purpose,' she raged. 'I think that's disgusting. And Cath helped you. Cath, my friend. You wait until I see her!'

'Shut up or be spanked. Brothers take precedence over friends, however close. Cath didn't want to be party to anything that might cause you pain but we both agreed, Harry and Ellen agree, even Mamma couldn't find any real objection, that you needed a little shock treatment.'

'Oh, how despicable!' Stephanie writhed, out of control.

'Stop that,' he said abruptly. 'You're getting me all stirred up.'

He didn't have to tell her. She could feel it in his taut body. 'I can't believe you've done this to me. The people I love. Does Laura know?'

'Good Lord, no.' He rolled his body half over hers. 'It's what you said, darling. Only the people who love you. It was a little bit cruel but it got results. You'll have me now at any price. I don't even think you'll object to marriage.'

'And Laura is going to marry ... Richard, is that right?'

'I think they're terribly well-matched. And she gets on so well with Julia.'

'So that's why you kissed her?' She pushed against his shoulders.

'I think I made her very happy.'

'You rat!'

'Don't, darling,' he said. 'I'm sorry. It's just that I'm not terribly good at waiting any more. God, I've known you since you were fourteen. Was there ever going to be an end to it? Then we had that setback with Marcus. How is he, by the way?'

'I could have him back in a minute,' she told him.

'I know it!' He laughed shortly and buried one hand in her hair. 'If you're going to be fair, Stephanie, you'll have to admit much of it was your fault. I understood your fears, but they had to go away.'

'You beast!' she whispered savagely, arching her back as his hard chest came in contact with her breasts.

'What a little hellcat!' He positioned his mouth over hers then began to kiss her with so many different pressures her body started to move under his hands. What did anything matter if he loved her? If she weren't so angry it would really be rather funny.

'Marry me before you drive me crazy,' he begged her.

'I'm not going to get engaged.'

'Neither am I.' His voice had slowed to a deep voluptuous drawl.

'And I would like to come to my husband a virgin.'

'What?'

'I think I would, that's all.'

'My God!'

'Are you angry?' Now she began to kiss him very tenderly, loving him, adoring him, worshipping him really.

'I'm not angry. I'm a whole host of things, but I'm not angry.'

'You can have me if you want me, of course. You've waited long enough.' She put out an apologetic hand.

'I'm rather intrigued by all this,' he suddenly said with a snort of laughter. 'Here I am maddened with passion and my little temptress has cooled off.'

'No, I haven't,' she lay back and looked up at him, her heart in her eyes.

'Would you mind straightening that robe.' With a few deft motions he did it for her. 'I suppose we ought to do it right. That's if I can survive that long.'

'I'll marry you just as soon as you like.'

'Oh, you'll do that and no mistake!' he said, back to his old dominance. 'I doubt if we could manage it under a month. Maybe even six weeks. Unless we run off?' He turned to stare down at her, a certain recklessness in his expression.

'It does sound good,' she said regretfully, 'but think how we'll disappoint everyone. Can you imagine what your mother would say? Cath? Then there's Harry and Ellen. They would be so disappointed. They've been with me through thick and thin. Come to think of it, there's practically the whole North. I mean a Ballinger has certain social obligations.'

'Do I take it then, we wait?' He was jerking the buttons of his shirt through the holes, the dangerous look tempered by a wry amusement.

'It won't be that long, darling.' She made a little face at him and he laughed.

'I still don't think you know how I feel about you.'

'You're everything in the world to me,' she said. 'You're the hero my young romantic heart settled on so long ago, you're an absolute tiger at times, you're devious and not above playing a few tricks. I love you whatever you are all the time. I've loved you for ten years without stopping. I'll love you for as long as I have breath in my body. I'm committed to one man and I'm ready to face real life with him.'

'That's my girl.' He came and sat on the side of the bed again, taking her face in his hands. 'My dear heart,' he said, very deeply in his throat, 'I'll wait.'

'Will you really?'

'I don't think you know whether to be glad or sorry?'

She could feel the faint trembling in his body. Or was that her own?

'Well, made up your mind? I'm absolutely mad for you but it might be in our best interests if I just get up and go.'

'I think you'd better,' she reached up to give him a quick, fiery kiss. 'I don't want you to ever take me boringly for granted.'

'Never!' He bit off a laugh. 'I shall never, ever, be able to do that.'

ROMANCE